GCSE
Science
EXAM REVISION NOTES

Keith Hirst

Philip Allan Updates
Market Place
Deddington
Oxfordshire
OX15 0SE

tel: 01869 338652
fax: 01869 337590
e-mail: sales@philipallan.co.uk
www.philipallan.co.uk

Design by Juha Sorsa
Cover illustration by Neil Fozzard
Artwork by Gary Kilpatrick
Printed by Raithby, Lawrence & Co Ltd, Leicester

P00254

Contents

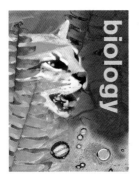

About this book

This book is for students following GCSE courses in Double Award Science. It covers the content of both Coordinated Science and Modular Science specifications. There are three sections covering biology, chemistry and physics. Each topic is contained in a double page spread and will usually comprise:

◆ **Key facts** — try to learn all these by heart.
◆ **Important ideas** — these are the scientific principles that you need to understand. In the examination, these ideas will often be tested by questions containing data such as graphs or tables. When you see a graph or a table in the examination, ask yourself 'Which idea is being tested here?'
◆ **Diagrams to remember** — many questions ask you to label diagrams, so you should try to learn all the labels provided here.
◆ **Equations and formulae** — up to 20% of the marks in the chemistry and physics sections of the examination paper will be for calculations based on the equations and formulae listed in the topics. Make sure that you know all these equations and formulae, particularly the units. Also make sure that you can use your algebra skills to transpose formulae.
◆ **Beware** — at the end of each topic there is a list of errors that many candidates make in the examination. Make sure you are not one of these candidates!

Revision skills

Revision progress

The first stage of your revision is to list all the topics of the specification. This will enable you to keep a check on which sections you have revised. Throughout your revision, assess how confident you are that you can answer questions on each topic. Here is one way of doing this, using the electricity and magnetism part of the specification as an example.

◆ Create a three-column table, as below.

Topic	Revised (N = none/P = part/A = all)	How confident am I? (1/2/3/4/5)
Potential difference	A	5
Energy in circuits	A	5
Mains electricity	A	3
Cost of using appliances	P	4
Electric charge	P	2
Electromagnetic forces	N	1
Electromagnetic induction	N	1

◆ List the topics in the first column and then complete the second column as you revise each topic.
◆ Assess yourself on the topic on a 1–5 scale: 5 if you are really confident about answering questions, 1 if you still have a lot of work to do.

Key words

There are more words to learn in the science specification than in a modern language specification such as French or Spanish. So why not make a vocabulary list for science? If you don't know what the words in the question mean, you will struggle to answer it!

Here is an example from a small part of the biology section of the specification. The bold words are science terms that you should be able to define.

The nucleus of a cell contains **chromosomes**. Chromosomes carry **genes** that control the **characteristics** of the body. Each chromosome carries a large number of genes. Many genes have different forms called **alleles**, which may produce different characteristics.

Make a vocabulary list like this:
Nucleus — controls the cell's activities
Chromosome — thread-like structures that carry genes
Gene — part of a chromosome that controls a characteristic
Characteristic — an observable feature

Mnemonics

There are many topics that you know quite well at nine o'clock on the morning of the exam, but once in the exam room you begin to panic and forget some of them. For facts that you may get the wrong way round, or in the wrong order, use a key called a mnemonic. Here are two examples.

OIL RIG should help you to remember:
Oxidation **I**s **L**osing electrons, **R**eduction **I**s **G**aining electrons

Run **O**ff **Y**ou **G**irls, **B**oys **I**n **V**iew should help you to remember the order of colours in the spectrum:
Red **O**range **Y**ellow **G**reen **B**lue **I**ndigo **V**iolet

But you will remember mnemonics far better if you compose your own.

At home

◆ Revise regularly — do *not* leave revision until near the examination.
◆ Plan your revision carefully, so there is no last-minute rush.
◆ Revise in a quiet room — you cannot revise properly if the TV is on or if a CD is playing.
◆ Revise in short stretches — work for half an hour, have a breather for 10 minutes, then start again.
◆ You should plan to revise for about 2–3 hours in an evening.
◆ Do 'active revision' — read a topic, close your book and make a summary from memory. Then go back and see what is missing from your summary.

Sample calculations

Proportion

The diagram shows what happens to the energy from grass which is grazed by a bullock.

(The diagram shows 3000 kJ of energy being eaten and 125 kJ being converted to new tissue.)

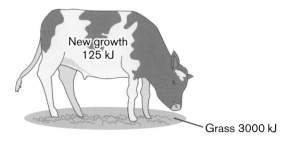

New growth 125 kJ

Grass 3000 kJ

What proportion of the energy in the bullock's food is converted into new tissues?

(2 marks)

One student's answer

Proportion of energy converted into new tissue $= \dfrac{125}{3000} = \dfrac{1}{24}$

◆ This is a good response because:
  • it shows the correct method
  • it gives the correct answer

Percentage

A scientist estimated the total energy flow per year through an ecosystem to be as follows:

Energy absorbed by producers   4 600 000 kJ per m^2 per year
Energy in sugars synthesised by producers   44 000 kJ per m^2 per year
Energy transferred to primary consumers   2920 kJ per m^2 per year
Energy transferred to secondary consumers   700 kJ per m^2 per year

Calculate the percentage of the energy absorbed by the trees that is transferred to sugar by photosynthesis. Show your working.

(2 marks)

One student's answer

$\dfrac{44\,000}{4\,600\,000} \times 100 = 0.96\%$

◆ This is a good response because:
  • it shows the correct method
  • it gives the correct answer

Using relative atomic mass

Calculate the formula mass (M_r) of iron(III) oxide (Fe_2O_3).
(Relative atomic masses: iron = 56, oxygen = 16)

(2 marks)

One student's answer
Number of atoms: iron = 2, oxygen = 3
Relative formula mass of iron(III) oxide = $(2 \times 56) + (3 \times 16) = 160$

◆ This is a good response because:
  • it shows the relative atomic mass of each atom
  • it shows the number of atoms
  • it gives the correct answer

Calculate the percentage of nitrogen in potassium nitrate (KNO_3).
(Relative atomic masses: potassium = 39, nitrogen = 14, oxygen = 16)   (2 marks)

One student's answer
Number of atoms: potassium = 1, nitrogen = 1, oxygen = 3
Relative formula mass of potassium nitrate = $39 + 14 + (3 \times 16) = 101$

Fraction of nitrogen in potassium nitrate = $\dfrac{14}{101}$

Percentage of nitrogen = $\dfrac{14}{101} \times 100 = 13.86\%$

◆ This is a good answer because:
  • it shows all the steps in the calculation
  • it gives the correct answer

Pressure

Some students made a machine which could lift a 100 N weight using a smaller
force. Calculate the pressure of the slave piston on the oil. (The slave piston had
an area of 20 cm².) Show your working.   (3 marks)

One student's answer
Pressure = force/area

Pressure = $\dfrac{100\,N}{20\,cm^2}$ = $5\,N/cm^2$

◆ The best way to answer this type of calculation question is to:
  • write down the equation
  • substitute the numbers in the equation
  (You can get marks for these first two stages even if you get the wrong answer.)
  • give the answer, including the unit

◆ This is a good response because:
  • all steps in the working are shown
  • the answer is correct
  • the unit of the answer is given

Exam skills

'Describe...'

You need to look carefully at the number of marks given for the question. If there are 2 marks, then you must give two points to gain full marks.

Example

Describe the function of the kidney. (2 marks)

One student's answer

The job of the kidney is to get rid of waste materials and to control the amount of water in the blood.

◆ This student's answer receives both marks because it makes two relevant points.

'Explain...'

Give the reasons *why*. There will usually be at least 2 marks for an 'explain' question, so you give at least two points.

Example

A student tested metal X by placing it in copper sulphate solution. The solution went a red/brown colour. Explain, as fully as you can, the results of the test. (2 marks)

One student's answer

Copper was displaced from the copper sulphate solution.

◆ This student's answer would receive only 1 mark because it only makes one point.
◆ To gain the second mark, the student should have stated *why* copper was displaced (because *metal X is more reactive than copper*).

'Suggest...'

Suggest means that you are not supposed to have learned the answer, but that you should be able to base your answer on scientific principles.

Example

Many prehistoric plants that are now extinct lived in swamps. Suggest one reason why these plants became extinct. (1 mark)

◆ You will almost certainly never have studied these plants. But you should be able to make suggestions based on the science you have studied. For example, you could write that *the climate changed and became too dry for them to survive*.

Extended writing

About 20% of the marks on your paper will be given for questions that require you to write two or more sentences. Use the number of answer lines and the number of marks as a guide to how much to write, but what you do write:
- must answer the question
- must use scientific words
- must flow, i.e. the sentences should be related to one another

Example (1)

Cotton crops can become infested with weeds. Scientists are developing genetically engineered strains of cotton which resist the action of herbicides. This means that when the crop is sprayed with herbicides, only the weeds are killed. However, there are potential dangers with this procedure. Cotton plants can interbreed with some other species of plants. Evaluate the possible advantages and disadvantages of developing genetically engineered, herbicide-resistant crops.   (5 marks)

One student's answer

An advantage is that the cotton plants should give a greater yield because fewer will die from the disease. This will lead to more profit for the farmer. A disadvantage is that if a weed breeds with a cotton plant, it might become resistant to the herbicide.

- This answer is good as far as it goes, but it only makes three points, whereas five marks are available.
- It should have gone on to explain why it would be a disadvantage for weeds to become herbicide-resistant.
- The question also asks for an evaluation. This means that you should come down on one side or the other and explain why.

Example (2)

Explain the scientific evidence for the big-bang theory for the origin of the universe.
                                                                                 (5 marks)

One student's answer

There are two pieces of evidence for the big-bang theory. Light coming from other galaxies is shifted towards the red end of the spectrum. Galaxies are moving away from each other.

- This answer receives only 2 marks because it makes only two points, neither of which is fully developed.
- The first point should have been developed by stating that the more distant galaxies show greater red-shifts.
- The second point should have been developed by stating that the more distant galaxies are moving away faster.
- The answer should then have concluded by stating that these two pieces of evidence indicate that the universe was once all in one place.

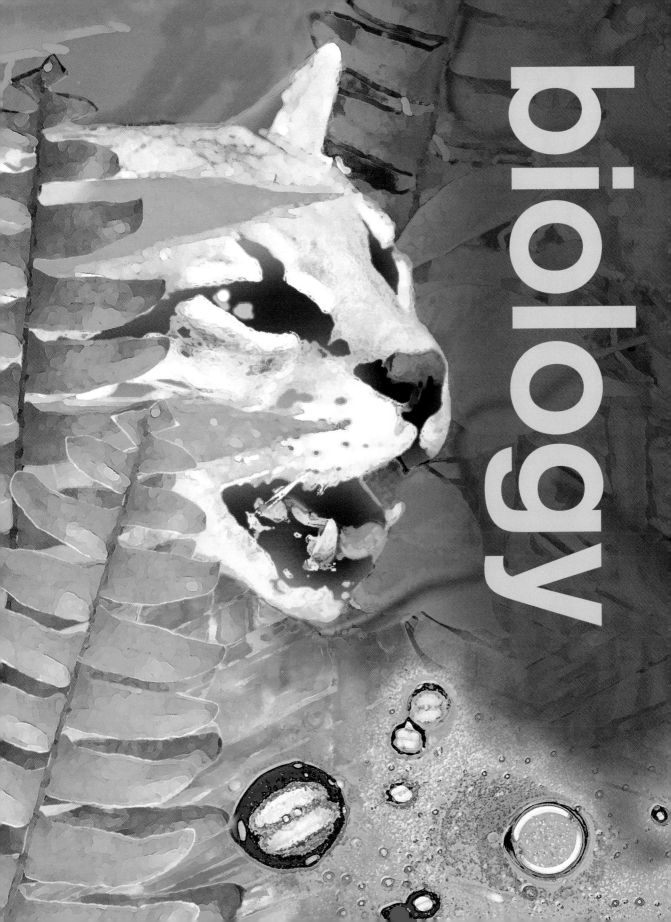

biology

Cells

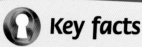

🔑 Key facts

Functions of parts of cells

- The **nucleus** controls the activities of the cell.
- The **cytoplasm** is where most of the chemical reactions take place.
- The **partially permeable membrane** controls the passage of substances into and out of the cell.

- The **mitochondria** are where most energy is released from chemical reactions.
- The **cell wall** strengthens plant cells.
- The **chloroplasts** in plant cells absorb energy from light to make food.
- The **large vacuole** in plant cells is filled with cell sap and helps to support the cell.

📈 Diagrams to remember

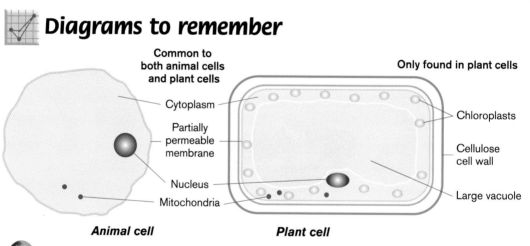

Common to both animal cells and plant cells

Only found in plant cells

Cytoplasm

Partially permeable membrane

Nucleus

Mitochondria

Chloroplasts

Cellulose cell wall

Large vacuole

Animal cell

Plant cell

💡 Important ideas

Diffusion

- Diffusion is the spreading of the particles of a gas, or particles in a solution, resulting in a net movement from a region where they are at a higher concentration to a region where they are at a lower concentration.
- The greater the difference in concentration, the faster the rate of diffusion.

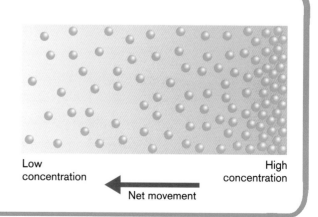

Low concentration

High concentration

Net movement

Osmosis

◆ Osmosis is the diffusion of water from a dilute to a more concentrated solution through a partially permeable membrane that allows the passage of water molecules but not the solute molecules.

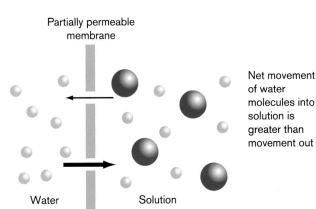

Partially permeable membrane

Net movement of water molecules into solution is greater than movement out

Water   Solution

Increasing surface area for exchange

◆ Many organ systems are specialised for exchanging materials. For example:
- the surface area of the lungs is increased by the alveoli
- the surface area of the small intestine is increased by villi
- the surface area of plant roots is increased by root hairs
- the surface area of plant leaves is increased by the flattened shape and by internal air spaces

Active uptake

◆ Substances are sometimes absorbed against a concentration gradient.
◆ This requires the use of energy from respiration.
◆ The process is called active uptake. Examples include:
- the uptake by plants of ions from the very dilute solution in soil
- the uptake of sugar from the intestine and ions from the kidney tubules

✖ Beware

◆ Don't use expressions such as 'it moves from a high concentration to a low concentration'. The examiner will not know what substance you are referring to, so write, for example, '**water** moves from a high concentration of water molecules to a low concentration of water molecules'.
◆ Don't forget to mention the **partially permeable membrane** when writing about **osmosis**.
◆ Don't forget to mention **energy from respiration** when writing about **active uptake**.

Digestion

Key facts

Where digestive juices are made and what they do

◆ Carbohydrase enzymes are produced in the salivary glands, the pancreas and the small intestine. These enzymes catalyse the breakdown of starch into sugars.

◆ Protease enzymes are produced by the stomach, the pancreas and the small intestine. These enzymes catalyse the breakdown of protein into amino acids.

◆ Lipase enzymes are produced by the pancreas and the small intestine. These enzymes catalyse the breakdown of lipids (fats and oils) into fatty acids and glycerol.

◆ The stomach also produces hydrochloric acid. This acid kills most of the bacteria taken in with food.

Diagrams to remember

The digestive system

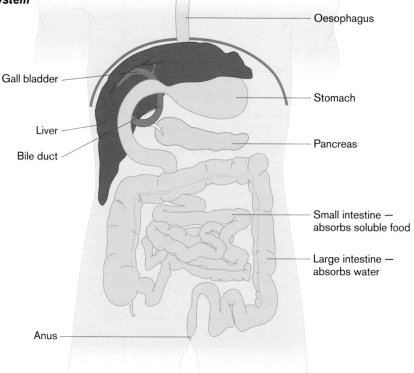

- Oesophagus
- Gall bladder
- Stomach
- Liver
- Pancreas
- Bile duct
- Small intestine — absorbs soluble food
- Large intestine — absorbs water
- Anus

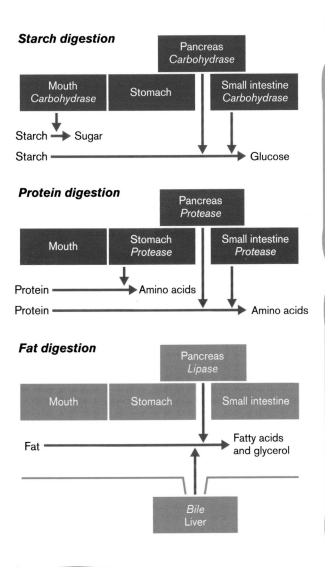

Starch digestion

Pancreas
Carbohydrase

| Mouth *Carbohydrase* | Stomach | Small intestine *Carbohydrase* |

Starch → Sugar

Starch ──────────────────────→ Glucose

Protein digestion

Pancreas
Protease

| Mouth | Stomach *Protease* | Small intestine *Protease* |

Protein ──────────→ Amino acids

Protein ───────────────────────→ Amino acids

Fat digestion

Pancreas
Lipase

| Mouth | Stomach | Small intestine |

Fat ──────────────────→ Fatty acids and glycerol

Bile
Liver

Important ideas

What digestion is

◆ Starch, proteins and fat are in-soluble. They need to be broken down into soluble substances so that they can be absorbed into the bloodstream by the wall of the small intestine.

◆ The breakdown of large mole-cules into smaller molecules is speeded up by enzymes.

What conditions are best for enzymes

◆ The enzymes in the stomach work best in the acid conditions provided by hydrochloric acid.

◆ The liver produces bile which is stored in the gall bladder before being released into the small intes-tine. Bile neutralises the acid that was added to food in the stomach. This provides alkaline conditions in which enzymes in the small intestine work best.

✖ Beware

◆ Don't confuse carbohydrate and carbohydrase. Remember that the names of digestive enzymes always end with -*ase*.

◆ Bile is *not* an enzyme — it does *not* break down fats into fatty acids and glycerol.

◆ Food does *not* pass through either the pancreas or liver on its way through the digestive system. The liver produces bile and the pancreas produces enzymes which both mix with the food in the small intestine.

Emulsification

◆ Bile also emulsifies fats (breaks large drops of fats into smaller droplets). This increases the surface area of fats for lipase enzymes to act upon, and so speeds up the rate of fat digestion.

Circulation

🔑 Key facts

The heart

◆ The atria receive blood — the right atrium receives deoxygenated blood from the body, the left atrium receives oxygenated blood from the lungs.

◆ The ventricles pump blood out of the heart — the right ventricle pumps deoxygenated blood via the pulmonary artery to the lungs, the left ventricle pumps oxygenated blood via the aorta to the body.

Blood vessels

◆ Arteries have thick walls containing muscle and elastic fibres. The muscle in their walls enables them to control the rate of blood flow to organs.

◆ Veins have thinner walls and often have valves to prevent the back-flow of blood.

◆ Capillaries have walls that are one cell thick.

Parts of blood

◆ Blood consists of a fluid called plasma in which are suspended white cells, platelets and red cells. Plasma transports:
 • carbon dioxide from the organs to the lungs
 • soluble foods, such as glucose and amino acids, from the small intestine to the organs
 • urea from the liver to the kidneys

◆ White cells have a nucleus. They help to defend the body against microbes.

◆ Platelets are small fragments of cells. They have no nucleus. They help blood to clot at the site of a wound.

◆ Red cells have no nucleus. They are packed with a red pigment called haemoglobin. They transport oxygen from the lungs to the organs.

📈 Diagrams to remember

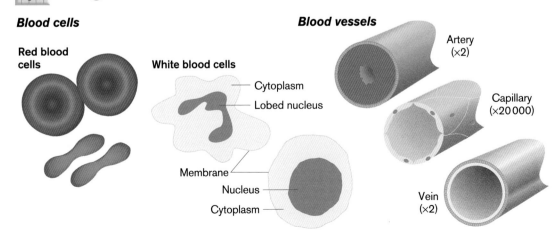

Blood cells

Red blood cells

White blood cells
— Cytoplasm
— Lobed nucleus
Membrane
Nucleus
Cytoplasm

Blood vessels

Artery (×2)

Capillary (×20 000)

Vein (×2)

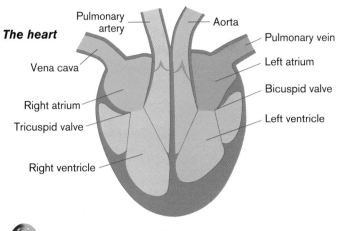

The heart

Pulmonary artery
Aorta
Vena cava
Pulmonary vein
Left atrium
Bicuspid valve
Right atrium
Tricuspid valve
Left ventricle
Right ventricle

Important ideas

Heart valves
◆ Valves prevent the back-flow of blood.
◆ The valves between the atria and the ventricles prevent blood flowing back into the atria.
◆ The valves at the base of the pulmonary artery and the aorta prevent blood flowing back into the heart.

Exchanges
◆ Substances needed by body cells, such as glucose and oxygen, pass out of the blood through the walls of capillaries.
◆ Substances produced by the cells, such as carbon dioxide and urea, pass into the blood through the walls of the capillaries.

Oxygen transport
◆ In the lungs haemoglobin combines with oxygen to form oxyhaemoglobin. In other organs oxyhaemoglobin splits into haemoglobin and oxygen.

haemoglobin + oxygen $\rightleftharpoons$ oxyhaemoglobin

Double circulation
◆ Blood flows from the heart to the organs through arteries and returns through veins.
◆ There are two separate circulation systems, one to the lungs and one to all other organs of the body.
◆ As blood flows through the lungs it loses carbon dioxide and gains oxygen — it becomes oxygenated.
◆ As blood flows through the organs of the body it loses oxygen and gains carbon dioxide — it becomes deoxygenated.
◆ Blood is returned to the heart after it has been oxygenated so that it can be pumped to the body at a high pressure.

Beware
◆ Arteries generally carry oxygenated blood while veins carry deoxygenated blood. However, remember the following exceptions to the rule: the pulmonary artery carries deoxygenated blood; the pulmonary vein carries oxygenated blood.
◆ Heart diagrams are drawn as *you* would see the heart, so the chambers on the right side of the diagram are the left atrium and left ventricle.
◆ Capillaries cannot constrict or dilate — their walls contain no muscle.
◆ White cells do *not* attack or fight with microbes.

Breathing and respiration

🔑 Key facts

Aerobic respiration (respiration that uses oxygen)

- All living cells in the body respire.
- Aerobic respiration inside cells occurs in mitochondria.
- During aerobic respiration, chemical reactions occur which:
  - use glucose
  - use oxygen
  - release energy
  - produce carbon dioxide

  glucose + oxygen →
  carbon dioxide + water (+ energy)

Anaerobic respiration (respiration that does not use oxygen)

- During vigorous exercise, muscle cells may be short of oxygen.
- They can then obtain energy from glucose by anaerobic respiration.
- The waste product from this process is lactic acid.

- The body then needs oxygen to break down this lactic acid.
- The oxygen needed for this is called an oxygen debt.

What energy is used for

- The energy that is released during respiration is used:
  - to build up larger molecules, using smaller ones
  - to enable muscles to contract
  - to maintain a steady body temperature
  - in active transport

📈 Diagrams to remember

The breathing system

Rib — Trachea
Muscle between ribs
Alveoli — Bronchus
Bronchiole
Heart
Diaphragm

Important ideas

Breathing

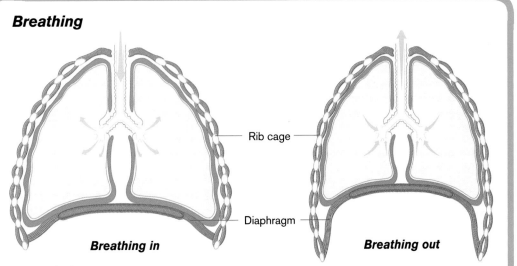

Rib cage

Diaphragm

Breathing in *Breathing out*

- To inhale:
  - muscles between the ribs contract, pulling the rib-cage upwards
  - the diaphragm muscles contract, causing the diaphragm to flatten
- These two movements cause an increase in the volume of the thorax.
- The resulting decrease in pressure results in atmospheric air entering the lungs.

✖ Beware

- Breathing and respiration are *not* the same.
- Carbon dioxide is *not* produced during anaerobic respiration in animals.
- Remember, when the *volume* of the thorax *increases*, the *pressure* inside *decreases*.
- Air is forced into the lungs by atmospheric pressure. It is *not* sucked in.

Recovering from the effects of exercise

- If insufficient oxygen is reaching the muscles, aerobic respiration cannot supply all the energy needs, so anaerobic respiration helps to make up the difference.
- Because the breakdown of glucose in anaerobic respiration is incomplete, much less energy is released than during aerobic respiration.
- Anaerobic respiration results in an oxygen debt which has to be repaid in order to oxidise lactic acid to carbon dioxide and water.

The nervous system

Key facts

Receptors

◆ Cells called receptors detect stimuli. These include receptors in the:
- **eyes**, which are sensitive to light
- **ears**, which are sensitive to sound
- **ears**, which are sensitive to changes in position
- **tongue** and **nose**, which are sensitive to chemicals
- **skin**, which are sensitive to pressure and to temperature changes

The eye

◆ Light enters the eye through the cornea.
◆ The cornea and the lens produce an image on the retina.
◆ The receptor cells in the retina send impulses to the brain along sensory neurones in the optic nerve.

Diagrams to remember

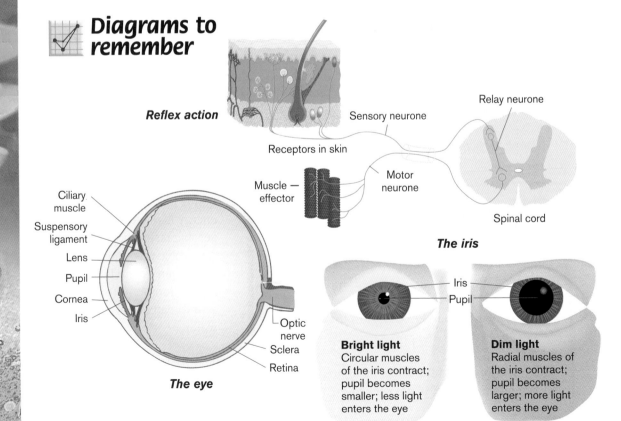

Reflex action

Receptors in skin

Sensory neurone

Relay neurone

Muscle — effector

Motor neurone

Spinal cord

Ciliary muscle
Suspensory ligament
Lens
Pupil
Cornea
Iris

Optic nerve
Sclera
Retina

The eye

The iris

Iris
Pupil

Bright light
Circular muscles of the iris contract; pupil becomes smaller; less light enters the eye

Dim light
Radial muscles of the iris contract; pupil becomes larger; more light enters the eye

Important ideas

Focusing

◆ To focus on near objects, the ciliary muscles contract and the lens becomes fatter.

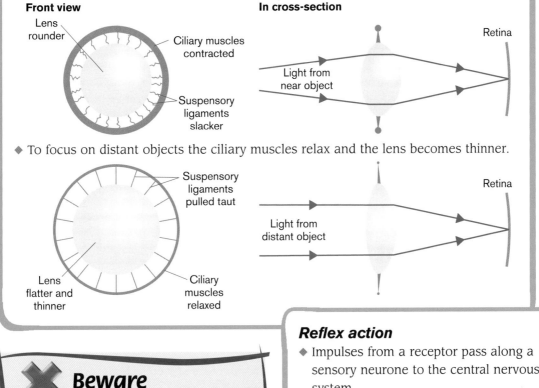

Front view

Lens rounder

Ciliary muscles contracted

Suspensory ligaments slacker

In cross-section

Retina

Light from near object

◆ To focus on distant objects the ciliary muscles relax and the lens becomes thinner.

Suspensory ligaments pulled taut

Lens flatter and thinner

Ciliary muscles relaxed

Retina

Light from distant object

Reflex action

◆ Impulses from a receptor pass along a sensory neurone to the central nervous system.
◆ At a synapse between a sensory neurone and a relay neurone in the central nervous system, a chemical is released which causes an impulse to be sent along a relay neurone.
◆ A chemical is then released at the synapse between a relay neurone and motor neurone in the central nervous system, causing impulses to be sent along a motor neurone to the effector, which brings about the response.
◆ The effector is either a muscle or a gland.
◆ A muscle responds by contracting, a gland by secreting chemical substances.

Stimulus → Receptor → Coordinator → Effector → Response

Beware

◆ It is the cornea, *not* the lens, where light is bent the most.
◆ Never talk about 'messages' — always state 'impulses'.
◆ In a reflex action involving parts of the head, impulses travel via the brain, *not* the spinal cord. Similarly for reflex actions involving the limbs, impulses travel via the spinal cord, *not* the brain.
◆ Sensory neurones are *not* receptors.
◆ Nerves and neurones are *not* the same: a neurone is a single cell, a nerve is a collection of neurones.

Hormones in homeostasis

Key facts

Hormones
- Hormones are chemicals. They are secreted by glands and are transported to their target organs by the bloodstream.
- They cause a response in their target organs.

- Hormones control many body processes.
- Blood sugar concentration is controlled by insulin and glucagon.
- Blood sugar concentration is monitored by the pancreas.
- The menstrual cycle is controlled by FSH, oestrogens and LH.

Important ideas

Regulation of blood sugar
- The blood glucose level is controlled by the hormones insulin and glucagon which are secreted by the pancreas.
- If the blood glucose level is too high, the pancreas secretes insulin which causes the liver to convert glucose into insoluble glycogen and store it.
- If the blood glucose level is too low, the pancreas secretes glucagon which causes the liver to convert glycogen into glucose and release it into the blood.
- Diabetes is a disease in which a person's blood glucose may rise to a fatally high level because the pancreas does not secrete enough of the hormone insulin.
- Diabetes may be treated by careful attention to diet and by injecting insulin into the blood.

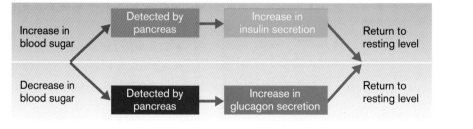

Control of the natural menstrual cycle

- ◆ Hormones in women control:
  - the monthly release of an egg from a woman's ovaries
  - the changes in the thickness of the lining of her womb
- ◆ Hormones involved in the maturation and release of an egg include:
  - FSH (secreted by the pituitary gland) which causes an egg to mature in one of the ovaries, and also stimulates the ovaries to produce hormones, including oestrogens
  - oestrogens (secreted by the ovaries) which inhibit the further production of FSH as well as stimulating the pituitary gland to produce a hormone called LH
  - LH (secreted by the pituitary gland) which stimulates the release of the egg about the middle of the menstrual cycle

The pituitary gland secretes FSH

FSH stimulates eggs to mature in the ovary

FSH stimulates the ovary to produce oestrogen

Oestrogen inhibits FSH production

Oestrogen stimulates LH production

✖ Beware

- ◆ The brain does *not* control blood sugar levels. This is done by the pancreas.
- ◆ Conversion of glucose to glycogen, and glycogen to glucose, occurs in the liver, *not* in the pancreas.
- ◆ The only hormone *causing* egg release is LH, *not* FSH or oestrogen.
- ◆ Progesterone is not on the specification. You will probably get confused if you try to learn it.

Artificial control of fertility

- ◆ Fertility in women can be controlled by giving:
  - FSH as a 'fertility drug', to a woman whose own level of FSH is too low, to stimulate eggs to mature
  - oral contraceptives that contain oestrogen, to inhibit FSH production so that no eggs mature

Homeostasis

🔑 Key facts

- Homeostasis involves controlling the internal conditions of the body in order to keep them constant.
- Internal conditions of the body that are controlled include **water content**, **ion content**, **blood sugar level** and **temperature**.
- Water leaves the body via:
  - the lungs when we breathe out
  - the skin when we sweat
- *Excess* water is lost via the kidneys in the urine.
- Ions are lost via the skin when we sweat.
- *Excess* ions are lost via the kidneys in the urine.

- Temperature is maintained at levels at which enzymes work best. Sweating cools the body when sweat evaporates, but water and ions are lost when we sweat.
- Blood sugar level is a good example of hormonal control.
- Waste products that have to be removed from the body include **carbon dioxide** and **urea**.
- Carbon dioxide is produced during respiration. It leaves the body via the lungs.
- Urea is produced in the liver by the breakdown of excess amino acids. It is removed by the kidneys in the urine. Urine is temporarily stored in the bladder.

📈 Diagrams to remember

The **brain** monitors and controls body temperature and monitors the water content of the body

The **skin** produces sweat which cools the body when it evaporates

The **liver** produces urea by breaking down excess amino acids

The **bladder** stores urine

The **pituitary gland** produces the hormone ADH which affects the volume and content of urine

The **lungs** get rid of most of the carbon dioxide when we breathe out

The **pancreas** monitors and controls blood glucose levels

The **kidneys** produce urine, which contains urea, excess water and excess ions, and they adjust the composition of urine

Organs involved in homeostasis

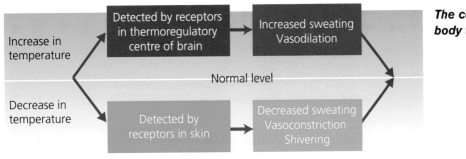

The control of body temperature

Important ideas

Sweating
- ◆ Receptors in the thermoregulatory centre in the brain are sensitive to a rise in blood temperature.
- ◆ The rate of sweating from sweat glands (effectors) increases.
- ◆ Evaporation of sweat cools the body.

Vasodilation
- ◆ Receptors in the thermoregulatory centre in the brain are sensitive to a rise in temperature of the blood.
- ◆ Muscles in the walls of arterioles (effectors) relax, causing the arterioles supplying the capillaries to dilate.
- ◆ More blood flows through the capillaries.
- ◆ The skin becomes flushed.
- ◆ More heat is transferred from the body to the environment.

Shivering
- ◆ Receptors in the thermoregulatory centre of the brain are sensitive to a rise in blood temperature.
- ◆ Skeletal muscles contract.
- ◆ The rate of respiration increases (energy is produced).
- ◆ Energy is transferred (some as heat).
- ◆ Blood flowing through the muscles is warmed.

Vasoconstriction
- ◆ Receptors in the skin are sensitive to a fall in temperature.
- ◆ Muscles in the walls of arterioles (effectors) constrict, so less blood flows through the capillaries.
- ◆ The skin becomes paler.
- ◆ Less heat is transferred from the body to the environment.

Beware
- ◆ Blood vessels do *not* move up and down in the skin.
- ◆ Capillaries do *not* constrict or dilate — it is the arterioles that supply them that constrict and dilate.
- ◆ Sweating does *not* in itself cool the body — cooling occurs when sweat evaporates.

Disease and drugs

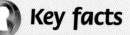 **Key facts**

Defending against the entry of bacteria

◆ The skin acts as a barrier.
◆ The breathing organs produce a sticky fluid called mucus which traps microbes.
◆ The blood produces clots which seal cuts.

White cells

◆ White cells defend against infective microbes by:
 • ingesting microbes
 • producing antibodies which destroy particular bacteria or viruses
 • producing antitoxins which counteract the toxins (poisons) released by microbes

 Diagrams to remember

Bacterial cell

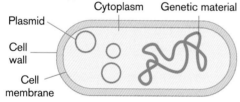

Plasmid
Cell wall
Cell membrane
Cytoplasm
Genetic material

Virus

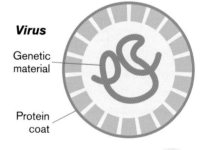

Genetic material
Protein coat

 Important ideas

Immunity

◆ People can be immunised against disease by introducing a mild, or dead, form of the microbe into their bodies.
◆ The white blood cells respond by producing antibodies which will help to defend the body against a future attack by the infective organism.
◆ If the microbe enters the body again, the white cells can produce antibodies much more rapidly than during the first attack.

Preventing microbes entering the body

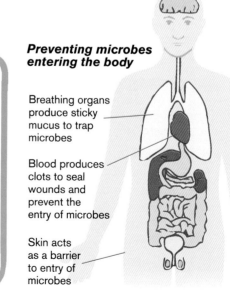

Breathing organs produce sticky mucus to trap microbes

Blood produces clots to seal wounds and prevent the entry of microbes

Skin acts as a barrier to entry of microbes

The effects of substance abuse

The brain is damaged by inhaling solvents and by excessive drinking of alcohol

Disease of the heart and blood vessels is caused by poisonous substances in tobacco smoke

Lung cancer, bronchitis and emphysema are caused by poisonous substances in tobacco smoke

The liver is damaged by inhaling solvents and by excessive drinking of alcohol

Drugs
◆ Solvents:
  • affect behaviour
  • damage the lungs, liver and brain
◆ Alcohol:
  • affects the nervous system by slowing down reactions
  • leads to lack of self-control, unconsciousness or even coma
  • damages the liver and brain
◆ Drugs
  • change the chemical processes in the body
  • may cause people to become dependent or addicted
  • may cause people to suffer withdrawal symptoms without them
◆ Tobacco smoke contains:
  • substances that can help to cause lung cancer and other lung diseases such as bronchitis and emphysema
  • substances that can help to cause disease of the heart and blood vessels
  • carbon monoxide, which reduces the oxygen-carrying capacity of the blood; this can deprive a fetus of oxygen and lead to a lower birth weight

✖ Beware
◆ Bacteria are trapped by mucus, *not* by cilia or hairs.
◆ White blood cells do not have battles with bacteria.
◆ Don't confuse antibodies and antitoxins — antibodies kill microbes, antitoxins neutralise toxins.
◆ Immunity is *not* caused by antibodies 'lasting a long time' but by rapid production of antibodies if the microbes re-enter the body.
◆ Tar from cigarette smoke does not 'block up the lungs', but it does contain chemicals that cause cancer.

Photosynthesis and growth

🔑 Key facts

Reactions during photosynthesis

◆ Light energy is absorbed by chlorophyll, found in the chloroplasts of plant cells.
◆ This energy is used to convert carbon dioxide and water into a sugar (glucose).
◆ Oxygen is released as a by-product.

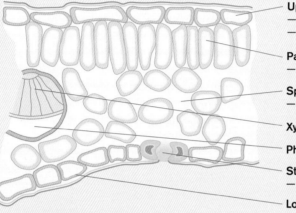

Upper epidermis
— secretes cuticle
— prevents excess water loss

Palisade mesophyll
— chloroplasts maximise light absorption

Spongy mesophyll
— air spaces to allow rapid diffusion of CO_2

Xylem — transports water and ions to leaf

Phloem — transports sugar out of leaf

Stoma
— allows gases to enter and leave leaf

Lower epidermis

Respiration in plants

◆ Plant cells respire using some of the glucose produced during photosynthesis.
◆ The energy released by plants during respiration is used to build up smaller molecules into larger molecules:
  • sugars into starch
  • sugars into cellulose for cell walls
  • sugars, nitrates and other nutrients into amino acids which are then built up into proteins
  • sugars into lipids (fats or oils) for storage in seeds

Hormones and plant growth

◆ Plant shoots grow towards light and against the force of gravity.
◆ Plant roots grow towards moisture and in the direction of the force of gravity.

◆ These responses are brought about by changes in the distribution of the hormones that bring about plant growth.

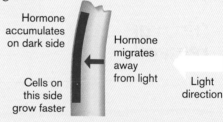

Hormone accumulates on dark side

Hormone migrates away from light

Light direction

Cells on this side grow faster

◆ Plant hormones are used by humans to:
  • produce large numbers of plants quickly by stimulating the growth of roots in cuttings
  • regulate the ripening of fruits on the plant and during transport to consumers
  • kill weeds by disrupting their normal growth patterns

Important ideas

Limiting factors

◆ The rate of photosynthesis may be limited by:
  • low temperature, which would happen in winter
  • shortage of carbon dioxide, which might happen around noon on a sunny day
  • shortage of light, which obviously occurs at night, but also perhaps at dawn and dusk

An example of a 'limiting factors' graph

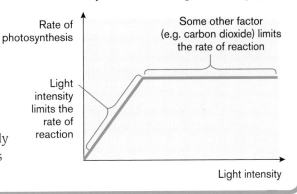

Why plants need mineral ions

Mineral ion	Function	Effect on plant of deficiency of ion
Nitrate	Synthesis of proteins	Stunted growth and yellow older leaves
Potassium	Helps enzymes involved in photosynthesis and respiration to work	Yellow leaves with dead spots
Phosphate	Important role in the reactions involved in photosynthesis and respiration	Poor root growth and purple younger leaves

 # Diagram to remember

Collecting the product of photosynthesis

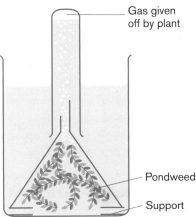

Gas given off by plant

Pondweed

Support

✖ Beware

◆ Plants photosynthesise when it is light, but respire 24 hours per day, *not* just at night.
◆ Chlorophyll is a green pigment; chloroplasts are structures that contain chlorophyll.
◆ Potassium and phosphate have similar functions and deficiency symptoms. Try to compose a mnemonic so that you don't confuse them.

Transport in plants

🔑 Key facts

- Water is absorbed through root hair cells by osmosis.
- Mineral salts are absorbed through root hair cells by active transport.
- Flowering plants have separate transport systems for water and nutrients.

- Xylem tissue transports water and minerals from the roots to the stem and leaves.
- Phloem tissue carries sugars from the leaves to the rest of the plant, including the growing regions and the storage organs.

✓ Diagrams to remember

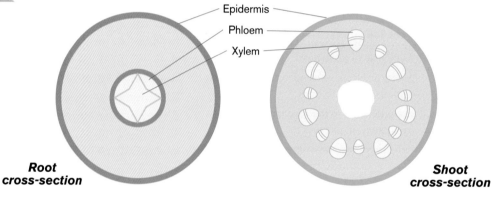

Epidermis
Phloem
Xylem

Root cross-section

Shoot cross-section

💡 Important ideas

Stomata

- Plants need stomata to obtain carbon dioxide from the atmosphere.
- Because of this, transpiration occurs mainly through stomata.
- The size of the stomata is controlled by guard cells which surround them.
- If plants lose water faster than it is replaced by the roots, the stomata can be closed to prevent wilting.

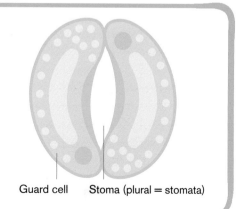

Guard cell   Stoma (plural = stomata)

Transpiration

- The loss of water vapour from plant shoots is called transpiration.
- Transpiration is more rapid in hot, dry and windy conditions.
- Most plants have a waxy layer on their leaves which stops them losing too much water.
- Plants living in dry conditions have a thicker layer of wax.

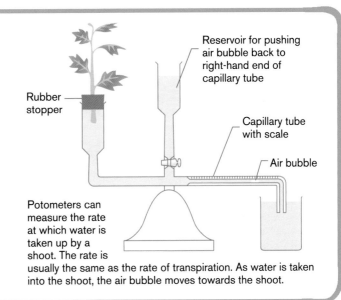

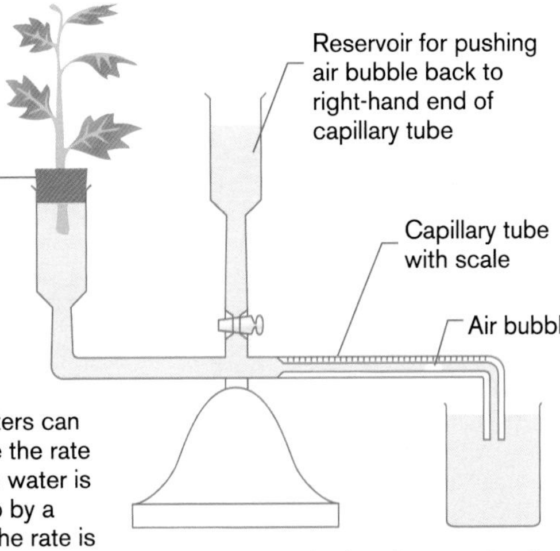
Reservoir for pushing air bubble back to right-hand end of capillary tube
Rubber stopper
Capillary tube with scale
Air bubble

Potometers can measure the rate at which water is taken up by a shoot. The rate is usually the same as the rate of transpiration. As water is taken into the shoot, the air bubble moves towards the shoot.

Turgor

- The water inside plant cells gives support for young plants.
- This is the main method of support for plant leaves.
- Plants wilt if the cells are short of water.
- When water moves into plant cells by osmosis it increases the pressure inside the cell.
- This pressure is called turgor pressure. It is turgor pressure that provides support.

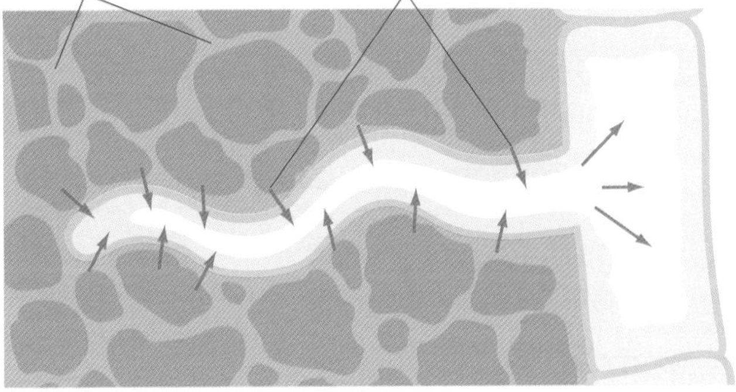
Soil solution surrounds the soil particles
Water moves into the root hair cell by osmosis

As water enters the root hair cell, the concentration of water in that cell becomes greater than the concentration in the next cell, so water enters the next cell by osmosis.

Beware

- Plants do *not* have stomata to allow transpiration. The function of stomata is to allow gases into the leaf, particularly carbon dioxide for photosynthesis.
- Don't confuse the functions of xylem and phloem. Compose a mnemonic for the transport of water by xylem and sugar by phloem.
- High humidity *decreases* the rate of transpiration.
- To remember the factors that affect the rate of transpiration, think of the best weather for drying clothes.

Genes and cell division

Key facts

- The nucleus of a cell contains chromosomes.
- Chromosomes carry genes that control the characteristics of the body.
- Each chromosome carries a large number of genes.
- Many genes have different forms called alleles, which may produce different characteristics.

Diagram to remember

Ovaries produce eggs by meiosis

Testes produce sperm by meiosis

Egg and sperm are both haploid

Fertilised egg is diploid

Fertilised egg divides by mitosis to produce diploid body cells

Important ideas

Sexual reproduction
- Sexual reproduction involves the joining (fusion) of male and female gametes.
- It results in individuals that have a mixture of the genetic information from two parents.
- These individuals show more variation than offspring from asexual reproduction because:
  - the gametes are produced from the parental cells by **meiosis**, which gives different combinations of alleles
  - when gametes fuse, one of each pair of genes comes from each parent
  - the genes in a pair may be different forms (alleles) and therefore produce different characteristics

Meiosis

◆ Cells in reproductive organs — testes and ovaries in humans — divide to form sex cells (gametes).
◆ When a cell divides to form gametes:
  • copies of the chromosomes are made
  • then the cell divides twice to form four gametes, each with a *single* set of chromosomes
◆ The daughter cells produced by meiosis have half the number of chromosomes compared with the parent cell.

Mitosis

◆ In body cells the chromosomes are normally found in *pairs*.
◆ Body cells divide to produce additional cells during growth.
◆ Before each cell division, a copy of each chromosome is made so that each body cell has exactly the same genetic information.
◆ The daughter cells produced by mitosis have the same number of *pairs* of chromosomes as the parent cell.

Asexual reproduction

◆ In asexual reproduction there is no fusion of cells and only one individual is needed.
◆ It gives rise to individuals whose genetic information is identical to that of the parent because they are produced by **mitosis** from the parental cells.
◆ These genetically identical individuals are known as **clones**.

Fertilisation

◆ When gametes join at fertilisation, a single body cell with new *pairs* of chromosomes is formed.
◆ A new individual then develops as a result of this cell dividing repeatedly by **mitosis**.

✖ Beware

◆ Flowers produce male and female gametes — seeds are produced by sexual reproduction, *not* asexual reproduction.
◆ Don't confuse mitosis and meiosis. You get no marks for hybrid spellings such as 'meitosis'.
◆ Remember:
  • **mitosis** keeps the number of chromosomes the same
  • **meiosis** halves the number of chromosomes
  • **fertilisation** doubles the number of chromosomes

Genetics, DNA and genetic engineering

🔑 Key facts

Genetic terms

◆ An allele that controls the development of a characteristic when it is present on only one of the chromosomes is a **dominant** allele.

◆ An allele that controls the development of characteristics only if it is present on both of the chromosomes is a **recessive** allele.

◆ If both chromosomes in a pair contain the same allele of a gene, the individual is **homozygous** for that gene.

◆ If the chromosomes in a pair contain different alleles of a gene, the individual is **heterozygous** for that gene.

◆ Parents may be **carriers** of a hereditary disorder without actually having the disorder themselves.

💡 Important ideas

Genetic engineering

◆ Genes from the chromosomes of humans and other organisms can be 'cut out' by using enzymes.

◆ These genes can then be transferred to other cells.

◆ The transferred gene continues to control the production of the same protein in the host cells.

Artificial selection

◆ Artificial selection is used to produce new varieties of organisms. This is done by choosing individuals that have useful characteristics and breeding from them. The same selection process is then carried out for many generations.

◆ The advantage of this selective breeding is:
  • it has resulted in varieties of plant and breeds of animal that have increased yields in agriculture

◆ The disadvantages of selective breeding are:
  • it greatly reduces the number of alleles and therefore the genetic variation in a population
  • further selective breeding to enable the species to survive changed conditions may not then be possible

DNA

- ◆ Chromosomes contain long molecules of a substance called DNA.
- ◆ Genes are sections of DNA molecules.
- ◆ DNA contains coded information which determines inherited characteristics.
- ◆ This coded information controls the order in which amino acids are assembled to produce a particular protein.

Cloning

- ◆ New plants can be produced quickly and cheaply by taking cuttings from older plants.
- ◆ These new plants are genetically identical to the parent plant.
- ◆ Modern cloning techniques include:
  - • tissue culture — using small groups of cells from part of a plant
  - • embryo transplants — splitting apart cells from a developing animal embryo before they become specialised, and then transplanting the identical embryos into host mothers
- ◆ The disadvantage of clones is that their wide-spread use in agriculture reduces the number of alleles available for selective breeding.

✘ Beware

- ◆ In sex determination there is a 50:50 chance of an X-carrying sperm or a Y-carrying sperm fertilising the egg — previous children have no bearing on this.
- ◆ There is no such thing as an X gene or a Y gene.
- ◆ Always use a capital letter (e.g. G) for the dominant allele and a lower case letter (e.g. g) for the recessive allele (choose letters that look different).
- ◆ Always use a Punnett square when answering genetic problems.
- ◆ DNA does *not* control the synthesis of amino acids. It controls their sequence in proteins.

Hereditary diseases

- ◆ Cystic fibrosis — a disorder of cell membranes — is caused by a recessive allele of a gene and can therefore be passed on by parents, neither of whom has the disorder.
- ◆ Huntington's disease — a disorder of the nervous system — is caused by a dominant allele of a gene and can therefore be passed on by only one parent who has the disorder.

The following Punnett square shows how two carrier parents can produce a child with cystic fibrosis

Each parent is heterozygous Ff

Gametes	F	f
F	FF	Ff
f	Ff	**ff**

25% chance of a child being **ff** and having cystic fibrosis

The following Punnett square shows how one parent can pass on Huntington's disease

One parent Hh, the other hh

Gametes	H	h
h	**Hh**	hh
h	**Hh**	hh

50% chance of a child being **Hh** and developing Huntington's disease

Sex determination

- ◆ In human body cells, one of the 23 pairs of chromosomes carries the genes that determine sex.
- ◆ In females the sex chromosomes are the same (XX).
- ◆ In males the sex chromosomes are different (XY).

Variation and evolution

Key facts

Variation

- Differences in the characteristics of different individuals of the same kind (species) can be due to:
  - differences in the genes they have inherited (genetic causes)
  - differences in the conditions in which they have developed (environmental causes)
  - a combination of both of these

Mutation

- New forms of genes result from changes (mutations) in existing genes.
- Mutations occur naturally.
- The chance of mutations occurring is increased by exposure to:
  - ionising radiations
  - certain chemicals
- Most mutations are harmful, sometimes causing uncontrolled cell division — cancer.
- Some mutations may increase the chances of survival of an organism.

Important ideas

Evolution

- The theory of evolution states that all species of organism evolved from simple life-forms which first developed more than three billion years ago.
- Darwin's theory of evolution by natural selection was only accepted gradually by other scientists.
- Darwinian theory (updated to take account of modern knowledge of genes) states:
  - individuals may show a wide range of variation because of differences in their genes — perhaps brought about by mutation
  - predation, disease and competition cause large numbers of individuals to die
  - individuals with *characteristics most suited to the environment* are more likely to *survive* and breed successfully
  - the genes that have enabled these individuals to survive are then passed on to the next generation
- This theory is summed up as 'survival of the fittest'.

Fossils

◆ Fossils are the 'remains' of plants or animals from many years ago which are found in rocks.
◆ Fossils may be formed:
  • from the hard parts of animals that do not decay easily
  • from parts of animals or plants that have not decayed because one or more of the conditions needed for decay are absent
  • when parts of the plant or animal are replaced by other materials as they decay
◆ Fossils have given scientists information about how much different organisms have changed since life developed on Earth.

Extinction

◆ Since life began on Earth, many species have become extinct.
◆ Species may become extinct due to:
  • changes to the environment (e.g. climate)
  • new predators
  • new diseases
  • new competitors

Trilobites lived hundreds of millions of years ago

Environmental conditions changed; they were not adapted to the new conditions and so became extinct

We only know about them from their fossilised remains in rocks

The peppered moth

◆ The peppered moth exists in two forms — white and black. The black form is the result of a mutation. Both forms are eaten by birds. In woods where the tree bark is light-coloured, the white form is camouflaged but the black form is not, so more black moths are eaten than white. In woods where tree bark is darkened by air pollution the reverse occurs. White moths are adapted to living in woods with light-coloured bark, so they are more likely to survive to breed. The reverse occurs in woods with darker bark. This is an example of natural selection occurring today.

✖ Beware

◆ Some mutations are *not* harmful — evolution would not occur without mutations.
◆ Fossils are most often formed from parts of animals that did not decay. Don't forget that decay needs oxygen.
◆ In answers to questions on extinction you must state that factors changed, e.g. *new* predators, *new* competitors, *new* diseases.
◆ In answers to questions on natural selection you must state how the distinctive features of an organism enabled it to survive rather than other organisms.

Adaptation and competition

🔑 Key facts

Adaptation

◆ You will probably be given questions about organisms you have not seen before and asked to suggest how they are adapted to their environment. Common examples are arctic animals and desert plants.

◆ Arctic animals are adapted to arctic conditions by having:
  • a large body size, but a small surface area through which they might lose heat, e.g. small ears
  • a thick, insulating coat
  • a large amount of body fat
  • camouflage, e.g. a white coat

◆ Desert plants are adapted to dry conditions by having:
  • small leaves to reduce water loss
  • a thick, waxy coat
  • long roots
  • water storage tissue

Competition – 'winners and losers'

◆ Plants compete with each other for:
  • space
  • water
  • nutrients from the soil
  • light

◆ Animals compete with each other for:
  • space
  • food
  • water

📈 Diagrams to remember

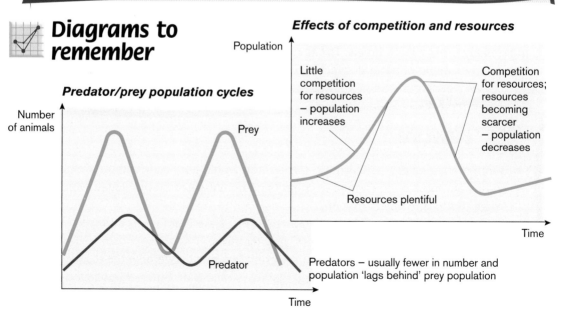

Predator/prey population cycles

Number of animals

Prey

Predator

Time

Effects of competition and resources

Population

Little competition for resources – population increases

Competition for resources; resources becoming scarcer – population decreases

Resources plentiful

Time

Predators – usually fewer in number and population 'lags behind' prey population

Important ideas

Population size

◆ You will often be given data to interpret. These data will usually refer to one or more of the following:
  • the total amount of food or nutrients available
  • competition for food or nutrients
  • competition for light
  • predation or grazing
  • disease

Predators and prey

◆ Animals that kill and eat other animals are called predators.
◆ The animals they eat are called prey.
◆ The numbers of both predators and prey are limited by the amount of food available.
◆ Predator–prey graphs usually show the following features:
  • if there is plenty of food for the prey, the prey population increases
  • if the population of prey increases, more food is available for its predators and their population may also increase
  • if the population of predators increases, more food is needed by them and the population of prey will decrease

◆ Zebra are preyed upon by lions. How are zebras adapted for escaping predation?

◆ The eagle is a bird of prey. How is it adapted for catching its prey?

✖ Beware

◆ In adaptation questions you will usually be given a drawing and asked to use information from it. You will only receive marks for features that can be seen on the drawing.
◆ The examiners will almost always use an organism you have not seen before — but neither have the other candidates — so make sensible suggestions.
◆ Predator–prey questions often appear along with food web questions. The predator you are asked about will usually feed on at least two prey species, or the prey you are asked about will usually be eaten by at least two predator species. You then have to work out what happens when the population of one species changes.

Human impact on the environment

🔑 Key facts

Land use

◆ Humans reduce the amount of land available for other animals and plants by building, quarrying, farming and dumping waste.

Pollutants

◆ Humans pollute:
  • water — with sewage, fertilisers or toxic chemicals
  • air — with smoke and gases such as sulphur dioxide
  • land — with toxic chemicals, such as pesticides and herbicides, which may be washed from land into water

Acid rain

◆ When fossil fuels are burned the following gases are released into the atmosphere:
  • carbon dioxide
  • sulphur dioxide
  • nitrogen oxides

◆ These gases dissolve in rain and can make it strongly acid.
◆ Acid rain can damage:
  • trees — causing leaf fall
  • rivers and lakes — making them strongly acidic so plants and animals cannot survive

Deforestation

◆ Forests are cut down:
  • for timber
  • to provide land for agriculture and homes
◆ The effects of deforestation are:
  • increased rate of carbon dioxide release into the atmosphere due to burning of branches and leaves and the activities of microbes that decay the roots and branches left behind
  • reduced carbon dioxide removal from the atmosphere
◆ Increases in the numbers of cattle and rice fields have increased the amount of methane released into the atmosphere.

💡 Important ideas

Greenhouse effect

◆ The levels of carbon dioxide and methane in the atmosphere are slowly rising.
◆ Carbon dioxide and methane in the atmosphere absorb much of the energy radiated by the Earth.
◆ Some of this energy is radiated back to the Earth and so keeps the Earth warmer than it would otherwise be — this is the greenhouse effect.

Fertilisers and eutrophication

◆ Farmers add fertilisers to soil to replace the nutrients that crops remove.

◆ Excess fertilisers might be washed into lakes and rivers and cause **eutrophication**.

◆ Eutrophication causes:
- the rapid growth of water plants
- death of some of these due to competition for light
- an increase in the number of microbes that feed on dead organisms
- the increased use of oxygen from the water by these microbes for their respiration
- the resultant suffocation of fishes and other aquatic animals

◆ Untreated sewage has the same effect on water as dead vegetation since it provides food for microbes.

✖ Beware

◆ Don't confuse fertilisers and pesticides.

◆ Fertilisers help crop growth by providing nutrients.

◆ Herbicides kill weeds.

◆ Insecticides kill insect pests.

◆ Don't forget that photosynthesis and respiration both affect the composition of the atmosphere.

◆ Photosynthesis removes carbon dioxide and adds oxygen.

◆ Respiration removes oxygen and adds carbon dioxide.

◆ Don't even mention the ozone layer when describing the greenhouse effect — there is no connection between the two.

◆ Don't forget that in eutrophication, most of the oxygen depletion is caused by respiration of the microbes that decay dead plants.

📈 Diagram to remember

The greenhouse effect

Carbon dioxide is a greenhouse gas

It prevents radiation that is reflected from the Earth from leaving the atmosphere – so warming the atmosphere

Acid rain

Sulphur dioxide and nitrogen oxides dissolve in rain to produce acid rain

Acid rain kills trees and freshwater organisms

Burning fossil fuels

Energy and nutrients

🔑 Key facts

♦ Green plants use light energy from the sun to convert carbon dioxide into carbohydrates.

♦ All living things respire, releasing carbon dioxide.

♦ All the energy in carbohydrates is eventually returned to the environment, mainly as thermal energy released by respiration.

♦ Plants use nitrates from the soil and carbohydrates to produce proteins.

♦ Bacteria and fungi in the soil convert proteins from dead organisms back into nitrates.

📈 Diagrams to remember

The nitrogen cycle

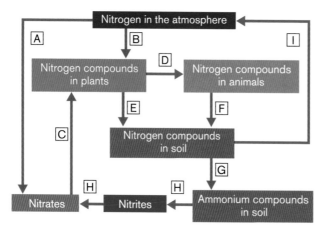

A Nitrates produced during lightning storms
B Atmospheric nitrogen fixed by nitrogen-fixing bacteria
C Nitrates absorbed by plant roots and combined with carbohydrates to produce proteins
D Plants eaten by animals
E Plants die
F Animals excrete and die
G Putrefying bacteria convert organic nitrogen into ammonium compounds
H Nitrifying bacteria convert ammonium compounds to nitrites, then nitrates
I Denitrifying bacteria convert organic nitrogen into atmospheric nitrogen

♦ The constant cycling of nitrogen is called the nitrogen cycle.

♦ In the nitrogen cycle:

• green plants absorb nitrogen in the form of nitrates from the soil

• plants use nitrates to make proteins

• when green plants are eaten by animals and these animals are eaten by other animals, some of the nitrogen then becomes part of the proteins in their bodies

• when putrefying (decay) microbes break down the waste products of animals, and the protein from dead animals and plants, ammonium compounds are produced

• nitrifying bacteria convert ammonium compounds to nitrates

$$\text{Plant protein} \xrightarrow[\text{putrefying bacteria}]{\text{death + decay}} \text{Ammonium compounds} \xrightarrow[\text{bacteria}]{\text{nitrifying}} \text{Nitrates}$$

The carbon cycle

◆ The constant cycling of carbon is called the carbon cycle.

◆ In the carbon cycle:

  • carbon dioxide is removed from the environment by green plants for photo-synthesis; the carbon from the carbon dioxide is used to make carbohydrates, fats and proteins which make up the body of plants

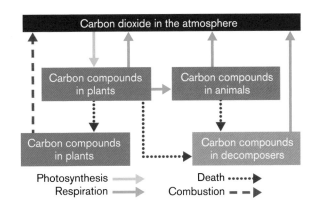

  • some of the carbon dioxide is returned to the atmosphere when green plants respire

  • when green plants are eaten by animals and these animals are eaten by other animals, some of the carbon then becomes part of the carbohydrates, fats and proteins that make up their bodies

  • when animals respire, some of this carbon becomes carbon dioxide and is released into the atmosphere

  • when plants and animals die, some animals and microbes feed on their bodies; carbon is released into the atmosphere as carbon dioxide when these organisms respire

 ## Important ideas

Energy flow

◆ Radiation from the sun is the source of energy for all living organisms.

◆ Green plants capture a small part of the solar energy that reaches them.

◆ This energy is stored in the substances that plants produce by photosynthesis.

◆ At each stage in a food chain, less material and less energy are contained in the biomass of the organisms, due to:

  • some materials and energy being lost in the organisms' waste materials

  • respiration

  • movement

  • heat loss to the surroundings

◆ These losses are especially large in mammals and birds whose bodies must be kept at a constant temperature which is usually higher than that of their surroundings.

Efficient food production

◆ The efficiency of food production can be improved by:

  • restricting energy loss from livestock by limiting their movement or controlling the temperature of their surroundings, so that food need not be respired to maintain body temperature

  • using hormones to regulate the ripening of fruits on the plant and during transport to consumers

Food chains and food webs

◆ Food chains show which organisms eat other organisms — A→B→C means that B eats A and C eats B.
◆ Food chains always begin with green plants (producers).
◆ Producers provide food for other organisms (consumers).
◆ Food chains are often interconnected to form food webs.
◆ Food chains and food webs show the transfer of energy and materials from one type of organism to another.

Decay

◆ Materials decay because they are broken down (digested) by microbes.
◆ Microbes are used by humans to bring about decay in compost heaps and in sewage works.
◆ Decay microbes work best when conditions are warm, moist and oxygen-rich.

Pyramids

◆ The number of organisms at each stage of a food chain can be shown as a pyramid of numbers.

Two examples of pyramids of numbers

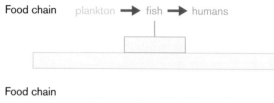

Food chain   plankton → fish → humans

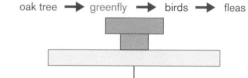

Food chain

oak tree → greenfly → birds → fleas

◆ The mass of living material (biomass) at each stage in a food chain is less than it was at the previous stage.
◆ The biomass at each stage can be drawn to scale and shown as pyramids of biomass.

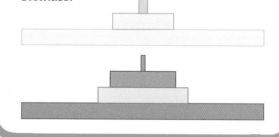

Beware

◆ Don't forget that detritivores (animals that eat dead material) and decay organisms both respire, returning carbon dioxide to the atmosphere.
◆ Don't confuse the different types of bacteria in the nitrogen cycle, and don't try to learn too much. Many specifications only require putrefying bacteria and nitrifying bacteria.
◆ Remember that mammals and birds use large amounts of food just to keep a high, constant body temperature. Most other types of animals rely on the sun to warm them up.

chemistry

Hazards and reactions

 Key facts

Safety precautions

- Protect the eyes by using goggles.
- Use rubber gloves to handle corrosive or irritant substances.
- Use a fume cupboard if irritant or toxic gases are given off in a reaction.
- Store inflammable substances away from oxidising substances in cool conditions.
- Store toxic substances under lock and key.

Diagrams to remember

You must remember what each of these hazard symbols means.

 Oxidising These substances provide oxygen which allows other materials to burn more fiercely.

 Harmful These substances are similar to toxic substances but less dangerous.

 Highly flammable These substances easily catch fire.

 Corrosive These substances attack and destroy living tissue, including eyes and skin.

 Toxic These substances can cause death when swallowed, breathed in or absorbed through the skin.

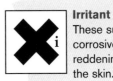 **Irritant** These substances are not corrosive but can cause reddening or blistering of the skin.

Make sure you can name simple pieces of equipment such as these...

 **Condenser**    **Tripod stand**    **Thermometer**    **Bunsen burner**

...and these.

Measuring cylinder

Funnel

Conical flask

 ## Important ideas

Tests for gases

Gas	Test	Positive result
Alkene	Bubble through bromine water	Brown coloured bromine water becomes colourless
Carbon dioxide	Bubble through limewater	Limewater turns cloudy
Chlorine	Place damp litmus paper in tube of gas	Litmus paper is bleached
Hydrogen	Place lighted splint in tube of gas	Gas burns with squeaky pop
Oxygen	Place glowing splint in tube of gas	Splint relights
Water vapour	Pass gas over anhydrous copper sulphate powder	White powder turns blue

Types of reaction

◆ **Cracking**: heating long-chain hydrocarbons with a catalyst to break them down into short-chain hydrocarbons.

◆ **Displacement**: when one element displaces another element from a compound, for example chlorine will displace iodine from potassium iodide.

◆ **Electrolysis**: using an electric current to decompose a liquid or a dissolved substance, for example breaking down water into hydrogen and oxygen.

◆ **Endothermic**: a chemical reaction that absorbs energy, for example a reaction that will not occur without heat being supplied.

◆ **Exothermic**: a chemical reaction that gives out heat energy, for example a combustion reaction.

◆ **Neutralisation**: the reaction between an acid and a base to form a salt and water.

◆ **Oxidation**: the addition of oxygen or the loss of electrons.

◆ **Reduction**: the removal of oxygen or the gain of electrons.

◆ **Reversible**: a reaction in which the products can react to form the original reactants, for example:

$$\text{nitrogen} + \text{hydrogen} \rightleftharpoons \text{ammonia}$$

◆ **Thermal decomposition**: the breakdown of a compound when it is heated, for example:

$$\text{calcium carbonate} \rightarrow \text{calcium oxide} + \text{carbon dioxide}$$

States of matter and atomic structure

🔑 Key facts

Atoms

- All substances are made of **atoms**.
- There are about 100 different sorts of atoms.
- A substance that contains only one sort of atom is called an **element**.
- Atoms have a small central nucleus made up of **protons** and **neutrons** around which there are **electrons**.
- The number of electrons in an atom is equal to the number of protons in the nucleus.
- Atoms have no overall electrical charge.

Particle	Relative mass	Relative charge
Proton	1	+1
Neutron	1	0
Electron	Negligible	−1

Atomic number and mass number

- All atoms of a particular element have the same number of protons.
- Atoms of different elements have different numbers of protons.
- The number of protons in an atom is called its **atomic number** (proton number).
- The total number of protons and neutrons in an atom is called its **mass number**.

- Atoms of the same element can have different numbers of neutrons; these atoms are called **isotopes** of that element.

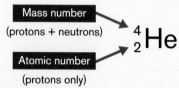

Mass number (protons + neutrons)

Atomic number (protons only)

$^{4}_{2}\text{He}$

Electrons

- Electrons occupy particular energy levels.
- Each electron in an atom is at a particular energy level.
- The electrons in an atom occupy the lowest available energy level.
- The arrangement of electrons in a sodium atom can be abbreviated to 2, 8, 1 which corresponds to the electrons in the first, second and third energy levels.

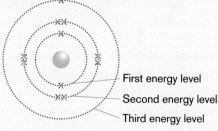

First energy level
Second energy level
Third energy level

- You should be able to draw the above type of diagram for the first 20 elements in the periodic table.

Diagram to remember

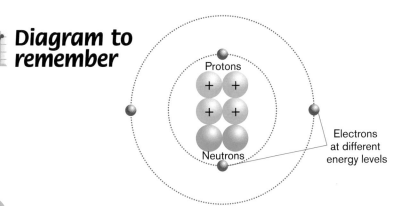

Protons

Neutrons

Electrons at different energy levels

Important ideas

States of matter

◆ If energy is supplied to a solid, its *particles vibrate more violently*; they may separate from each other and become free to move — this is **melting**.
◆ The temperature at which a solid melts is called the melting point.
◆ Heating a liquid makes its *particles move around more quickly*.
◆ Particles that have enough energy may overcome attractive forces and escape from the liquid and become a gas — this is **evaporation**.
◆ When the temperature is higher, more particles have enough energy to escape so evaporation is faster.
◆ If the temperature is high enough, a liquid will **boil**.
◆ The temperature at which a liquid boils is called its boiling point.

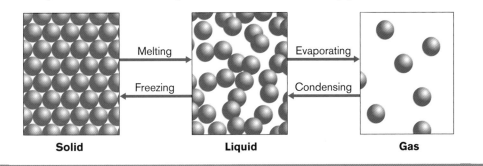

Solid		Liquid		Gas
	Melting →		Evaporating →	
	← Freezing		← Condensing	

Beware

◆ Remember the difference between atomic number and mass number. Compose a mnemonic to help you.
◆ Don't mix up the way in which particles move:
  • particles in solids vibrate
  • particles in liquids move around fairly slowly at room temperature
  • particles in gases move around quickly at room temperature

Ions and ionic compounds

Key facts

Compounds

- Compounds are substances in which atoms of two, or more, elements are not just mixed together but chemically combined.
- Chemical reactions between elements involve either the giving and taking of electrons *or* the sharing of electrons in the highest occupied energy levels of atoms.

Ions

- When atoms form chemical bonds by gaining and losing electrons, they form electrically charged atoms called **ions**.

- The atoms that *lose electrons* become *positively charged* ions.
- The atoms that *gain electrons* become *negatively charged* ions.
- These ions now have the electronic structure of a noble gas.

You should be able to draw ions in the following way:

Sodium ion (Na⁺)

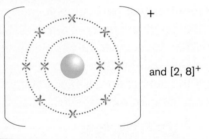

and $[2, 8]^+$

Important ideas

Ionic compounds

- An ionic compound is a **giant structure** of ions.
- Ionic compounds are held together by strong forces of attraction between oppositely charged ions — this is the **ionic bond**.
- Ionic compounds form regular structures (giant ionic lattices) in which there are *strong forces between oppositely charged ions*.
- The strong forces result in these compounds having *high melting points and high boiling points*.
- When they are melted or dissolved in water, ionic compounds conduct electricity because the *ions are free to move*.

Strong ionic bonds (electrostatic attraction between oppositely charged ions)

The formation of sodium chloride

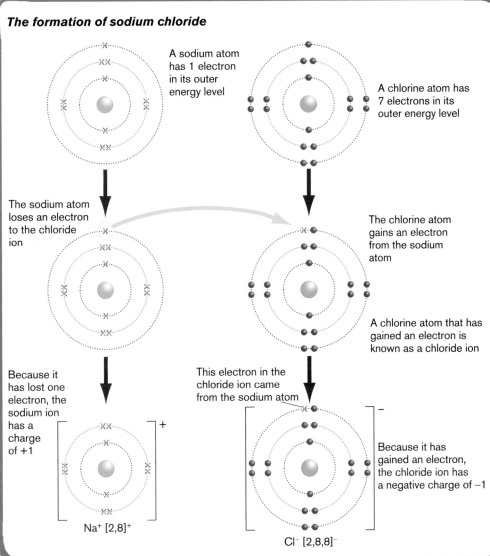

A sodium atom has 1 electron in its outer energy level

A chlorine atom has 7 electrons in its outer energy level

The sodium atom loses an electron to the chloride ion

The chlorine atom gains an electron from the sodium atom

A chlorine atom that has gained an electron is known as a chloride ion

Because it has lost one electron, the sodium ion has a charge of +1

This electron in the chloride ion came from the sodium atom

Because it has gained an electron, the chloride ion has a negative charge of −1

Na^+ [2,8]$^+$

Cl^- [2,8,8]$^-$

Some ions to remember

Positively charged ions		Negatively charged ions	
Hydrogen	H^+	Chloride	Cl^-
Sodium	Na^+	Bromide	Br^-
Potassium	K^+	Iodide	I^-
Lithium	Li^+	Hydroxide	OH^-
Ammonium	NH_4^+	Nitrate	NO_3^-
Calcium	Ca^{2+}	Oxide	O^{2-}
Magnesium	Mg^{2+}	Sulphate	SO_4^{2-}
Aluminium	Al^{3+}	Carbonate	CO_3^{2-}
Iron(III)	Fe^{3+}	Phosphate	PO_4^{3-}

Covalent molecules

🔑 Key facts

- Atoms can form bonds by sharing electrons.
- Atoms that share electrons often form **molecules**.
- The atoms in molecules are held together because they *share pairs of electrons*.
- The strong bonds between the atoms are called **covalent bonds**.

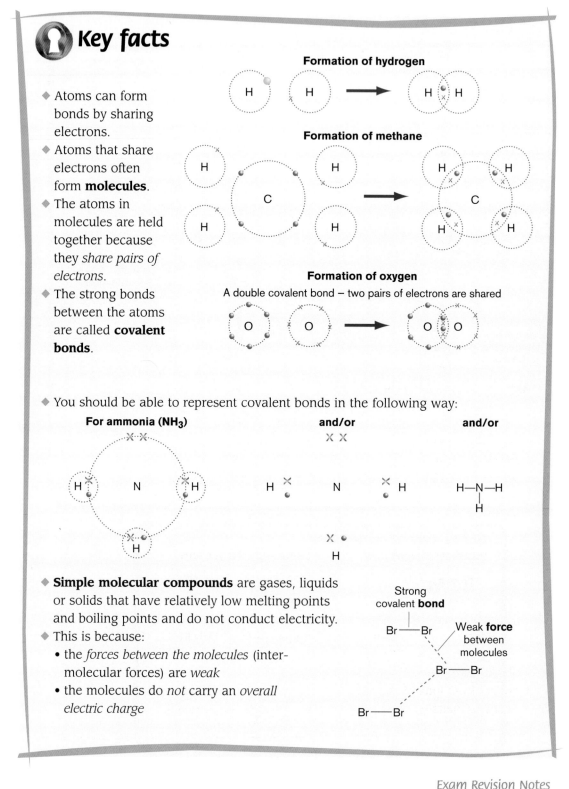

Formation of hydrogen

Formation of methane

Formation of oxygen

A double covalent bond – two pairs of electrons are shared

- You should be able to represent covalent bonds in the following way:

For ammonia (NH₃)   **and/or**   **and/or**

- **Simple molecular compounds** are gases, liquids or solids that have relatively low melting points and boiling points and do not conduct electricity.
- This is because:
  - the *forces between the molecules* (inter-molecular forces) are *weak*
  - the molecules do *not* carry an *overall electric charge*

Strong covalent **bond**

Br —— Br   Weak **force** between molecules

Br —— Br

Br —— Br

💡 Important ideas

Giant covalent structures

◆ Atoms that share electrons can also form giant structures.

◆ Diamond and graphite (forms of carbon) and silicon dioxide (silica) are giant covalent structures (lattices) of atoms.

◆ Because of the large number of covalent bonds in their structures, they have very high melting points.

◆ In graphite, the carbon atoms form layers which are free to slide over each other. There are free electrons which allow graphite to conduct electricity.

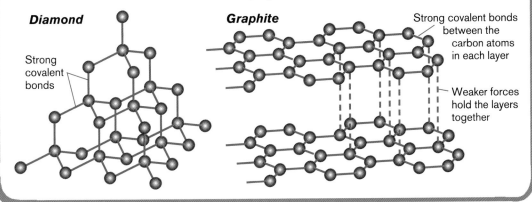

Diamond

Strong covalent bonds

Graphite

Strong covalent bonds between the carbon atoms in each layer

Weaker forces hold the layers together

Metals as giant structures

◆ Metals consist of giant structures in which the *electrons* from the highest occupied (outer) energy levels of metal atoms are *free to move* through the whole structure.

◆ These free electrons:
  • hold the atoms together in a regular structure
  • allow the atoms to slide over each other
  • allow the metal to conduct heat and electricity

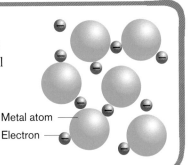

Metal atom

Electron

❌ Beware

◆ Don't confuse the strong covalent bonds, which hold atoms together to form giant covalent molecules such as diamond, with the weak bonds that exist between one covalent molecule and another, for example between two molecules of water.

◆ Make sure you can draw:
  • ions from ionic compounds
  • shared pairs of electrons in covalent compounds — practise drawing hydrogen molecules, chlorine molecules and water molecules

Useful products from oil

🔑 Key facts

How crude oil was formed

- ◆ Crude oil was formed from the remains of organisms that lived millions of years ago.
- ◆ It was formed:
  - by the action of heat and pressure
  - over millions of years
  - in the absence of air

Fractional distillation

- ◆ Crude oil is a mixture of a very large number of compounds. These can be separated by fractional distillation:
  - crude oil is heated
  - the oil evaporates, forming a gas
  - the gas is allowed to condense at different temperatures in a fractionating column

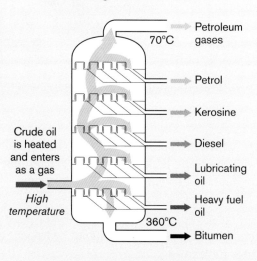

- ◆ Most of the compounds in crude oil consist of molecules made up of hydrogen and carbon atoms only (**hydrocarbons**).
- ◆ Each fraction obtained from the fractionating column contains molecules with a similar number of carbon atoms.
- ◆ The larger the molecules (the greater the number of carbon atoms) in a hydrocarbon:
  - the higher its boiling point
  - the less volatile it is
  - the less easily it flows (the more viscous it is)
  - the less easily it ignites (the less flammable it is)
- ◆ Hydrocarbons with large molecules are not very useful as fuels.
- ◆ They can be broken down ('cracked') to produce smaller, more useful molecules.
- ◆ This process involves heating the hydrocarbons to vaporise them and passing the vapours over a hot catalyst.
- ◆ Short-chain hydrocarbons from cracking are useful for:
  - fuels
  - making plastics (polymers) such as poly(ethene) and poly(propene)

Important ideas

Alkanes

◆ When the carbon atoms in a hydrocarbon are joined by *single* covalent carbon–carbon bonds they are known as **alkanes**.

◆ Alkanes are **saturated** hydro-carbons.

Alkenes

◆ **Alkenes** are hydrocarbons with carbon–carbon *double* covalent bonds.

◆ They are **unsaturated** hydro-carbons.

Polymers

◆ Alkenes are reactive and so are useful for making many other substances, including polymers.

◆ Polymers are very large molecules, and are formed when many small molecules, called **monomers**, join together.

◆ This process is called **polymerisation**.

◆ When unsaturated monomers join together to form a polymer with no other substance being produced in the reaction, the process is called **addition polymerisation**.

◆ Plastics are polymers and are made by polymerisation. For example, poly(ethene) (often called polythene) is made by polymerising the simplest alkene, ethene.

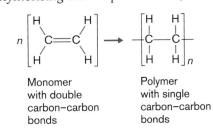

Monomer with double carbon–carbon bonds

Polymer with single carbon–carbon bonds

Beware

◆ Compose a mnemonic to help you remember the difference between alkanes and alkenes (single C–C bonds versus double C=C bonds).

◆ Note the conventions used when drawing the formulae for polymerisation reactions:
 • the '*n*' goes outside the brackets on the middle left of the monomer (alkene)
 • the '*n*' goes outside the bracket on the bottom right of the polymer
 For example:

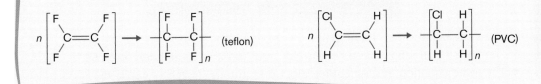

Extracting metals from ores

Key facts

Reactivity of metals

- In ores, the metal or metal compound is concentrated enough to make it economic to extract the metal.
- Often an ore contains a metal oxide.
- To extract the metal, the oxygen must be removed from the metal oxide. This is called **reduction**.
- How a metal is extracted from its ore depends on how reactive the metal is.

- The reactivity series of metals lists them in order of their reactivity, the most reactive metal being placed at the top of the list and the least reactive at the bottom.
- A more reactive metal can displace a less reactive metal from its compounds.
- The non-metallic elements carbon and hydrogen will also displace less reactive metals from oxides of those metals.

Important ideas

Extracting aluminium

- Aluminium is more reactive than carbon or hydrogen, so these cannot be used to reduce aluminium oxide.
- Because aluminium oxide has a very high melting point it is dissolved in a molten aluminium compound called cryolite, at a much lower temperature.
- The electrodes are made of carbon.
- The aluminium forms at the negative electrode.
- Oxygen forms at the positive electrodes. This makes the positive electrodes burn away quickly, so they have to be replaced frequently.

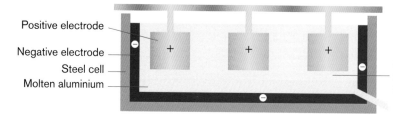

- The ionic equation at the negative electrode (cathode) is $Al^{3+} + 3e^- \rightarrow Al$
- The aluminium ions have received electrons, so they have been reduced.
- The ionic equation at the positive electrode (anode) is $2O^{2-} - 4e^- \rightarrow O_2$

Extracting iron

◆ Iron is less reactive than carbon, so it can be extracted from its ore using carbon in a blast furnace.
◆ Hot air is blown into the furnace and this causes the coke to burn, forming carbon dioxide and releasing energy.

$$C(s) + O_2(g) \rightarrow CO_2(g)$$

◆ At the high temperatures in the furnace the carbon dioxide reacts with coke to form carbon monoxide.

$$CO_2(g) + C(s) \rightarrow 2CO(g)$$

◆ The carbon monoxide **reduces** the iron oxide in the iron ore into molten iron, which then flows to the bottom of the furnace.

$$Fe_2O_3(s) + 3CO(g) \rightarrow 2Fe(l) + 3CO_2(g)$$

◆ Limestone is added to remove acidic impurities, forming a molten slag which floats on the surface of the molten iron.

Purifying copper

◆ Copper can be purified by electrolysis using a positive electrode made of the impure copper and a negative electrode of pure copper in a solution containing copper ions.
◆ At the negative electrode copper ions gain electrons — reduction.

$$Cu^{2+} + 2e^- \rightarrow Cu$$

◆ At the positive electrode copper atoms lose electrons — oxidation.

$$Cu - 2e^- \rightarrow Cu^{2+}$$

+ −

Impure copper anode – gets smaller

Pure copper cathode – gets larger

Solution containing copper ions

Electrolysis

◆ When substances that are made of ions are dissolved in water, or melted, they can be broken down into simpler substances by passing an electric current through them.
◆ This chemical process is called **electrolysis**.
◆ During electrolysis, positively charged metal ions move to the negative electrode (cathode), and negatively charged ions move to the positive electrode (anode).

✖ Beware

◆ Always check the reactivity series in your Data Book/Sheet. If the metal is above carbon and hydrogen it *cannot* be extracted by reducing the oxide.
◆ Don't forget that it is *carbon monoxide* which *reduces* iron oxide in the blast furnace.
◆ Make sure that you learn the ionic equations for the aluminium cell and the copper cell — you are almost certain to get one of them in the exam.
◆ Use a mnemonic like OIL RIG to remind you that Oxidation Is Losing electrons and Reduction Is Gaining electrons.

Useful products from limestone and air

🔑 Key facts

Using limestone

- Limestone is mainly calcium carbonate.
- Its formula is $CaCO_3$.
- Limestone is used:
  - as a building material
  - to neutralise acidity in lakes and soils
  - to make cement
  - to make glass

Using air

- Air is almost 80% nitrogen.
- Converting this nitrogen into useful compounds is very difficult, but it can be used to manufacture ammonia.
- Ammonia can be oxidised to produce nitric acid.

💡 Important ideas

Quicklime

- Limestone is heated in a kiln to break it down into quicklime (calcium oxide) and carbon dioxide.
  $$CaCO_3(s) \rightarrow CaO(s) + CO_2(g)$$
- This type of reaction is called **thermal decomposition**.
- Quicklime reacts with water to produce slaked lime (calcium hydroxide), which is used to reduce the acidity of soil and lakes.

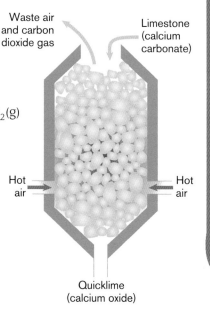

Waste air and carbon dioxide gas

Limestone (calcium carbonate)

Hot air

Hot air

Quicklime (calcium oxide)

Cement

- Cement is produced by roasting powdered limestone with powdered clay in a rotary kiln.
- When cement is mixed with water, sand and crushed rock, a hard, stone-like building material called concrete is produced.

Glass

◆ Glass is made by heating a mixture of limestone, sand and soda (sodium carbonate).

Fertilisers

◆ Ammonia can be oxidised to produce nitric acid.
◆ Ammonia gas reacts with oxygen in air in the presence of a hot platinum catalyst.
◆ This oxidation reaction forms nitrogen monoxide which is then cooled and reacted with water and more oxygen to form nitric acid.
◆ Ammonium nitrate fertiliser is made by the neutralisation reaction between ammonia and nitric acid.
◆ Nitrogen-based fertilisers are important in agriculture for increasing the yields of crops.

The Haber process for manufacturing ammonia

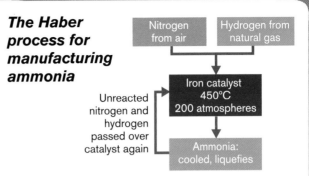

◆ The reaction is reversible. This means that ammonia also breaks back down again into nitrogen and hydrogen.

$$N_2(g) + 3H_2(g) \rightleftharpoons 2NH_3(g)$$

◆ An equilibrium occurs when the forward and reverse reactions proceed at the same rate.
◆ The reaction conditions are chosen to produce a reasonable yield of ammonia quickly.
◆ Higher temperatures speed up the reaction, but reduce the percentage of ammonia in the equilibrium mixture — this is because the reaction is **exothermic.**
◆ High pressures increase the percentage of ammonia in the equilibrium mixture, but the cost of the chemical plant makes using very high pressures uneconomic.

✖ Beware

◆ Revise plant nutrition and eutrophication from the biology section of the specification when you revise this topic.
◆ You are almost certain to get a question on the Haber process.
◆ Don't confuse the effects of temperature and pressure on the *rate* of the reaction with the effects of temperature and pressure on the *percentage of ammonia in the equilibrium mixture.*
◆ Increases in both temperature and pressure increase the rate of the reaction, *but* increasing temperature decreases the percentage of ammonia in the equilibrium mixture, whereas increasing the pressure increases the percentage of ammonia in the equilibrium mixture.
◆ The conditions chosen are therefore a compromise.

Representing reactions

🔑 Key facts

Symbols

◆ Each element is represented by a different symbol. For example, Fe is the symbol for iron.

◆ The symbols for elements are used to write chemical formulae for compounds. These show the ratios of atoms of different elements which are combined to form the compounds. For example, the formula of ammonia is NH_3 — this means that each ammonia molecule contains 1 atom of nitrogen and 3 atoms of hydrogen.

Word equations

◆ If you are asked to write a word equation you are usually given the names of all the substances involved.

◆ For example, calcium oxide and carbon dioxide are formed by the thermal decomposition of calcium carbonate. If you were asked to write a word equation for this reaction you would do so using the following rules:

• calcium carbonate is the reactant, so it goes on the left-hand side of the equation
• calcium oxide and carbon dioxide are products, so they go on the right-hand side of the equation
• therefore the word equation is

calcium carbonate →
calcium oxide + carbon dioxide

State symbols

◆ (aq) means a substance is dissolved in water, (g) a gas, (l) a liquid, (s) a solid.

◆ For example, in the equation
$CaCO_3(s) \rightarrow CaO(s) + CO_2(g)$,
$CaCO_3$ and CaO are solids and CO_2 is a gas.

💡 Important ideas

Balancing ionic equations

◆ During electrolysis, ions gain or lose electrons at the electrodes.
◆ Electrically neutral atoms or molecules are released.
◆ For example, if you were asked to balance the ionic equation for the production of aluminium during electrolysis

$$Al^{3+} + ...e^- \rightarrow ...$$

you would do so as follows:

• the number of electrons must equal the number of positive charges on the aluminium, i.e. 3
• the aluminium produced is electrically neutral, i.e. Al

$$Al^{3+} + 3e^- \rightarrow Al$$

Representing reactions

◆ **Displacement** occurs when a more reactive element displaces a less reactive element from one of its compounds, for example chlorine will displace iodine from potassium iodide solution:

$$\text{potassium iodide} + \text{chlorine} \rightarrow \text{potassium chloride} + \text{iodine}$$
$$2KI_{(aq)} + Cl_2{(g)} \rightarrow 2KCl_{(aq)} + I_2{(s)}$$

◆ **Electrolysis** involves using an electric current to decompose a liquid or a dissolved substance, for example electrolysis of sodium chloride solution:

$$\text{Positive electrode} \quad 2Cl^-{(aq)} - 2e^- \rightarrow Cl_2{(g)}$$
$$\text{Negative electrode} \quad 2H^+{(aq)} + 2e^- \rightarrow H_2{(g)}$$

◆ **Neutralisation** is the reaction between an acid and a base to form a salt and water, for example the reaction between hydrochloric acid and sodium hydroxide:

$$\text{hydrochloric acid} + \text{sodium hydroxide} \rightarrow \text{sodium chloride} + \text{water}$$
$$HCl_{(aq)} + NaOH_{(aq)} \rightarrow NaCl_{(aq)} + H_2O_{(l)}$$
$$H^+{(aq)} + OH^-{(aq)} \rightarrow H_2O_{(l)}$$

◆ **Oxidation** is the addition of oxygen, for example the combustion of carbon:

$$\text{carbon} + \text{oxygen} \rightarrow \text{carbon dioxide}$$
$$C_{(s)} + O_2{(g)} \rightarrow CO_2{(g)}$$

◆ **Reduction** is the removal of oxygen, for example using carbon to reduce lead oxide:

$$\text{lead oxide} + \text{carbon} \rightarrow \text{lead} + \text{carbon dioxide}$$
$$2PbO_{(s)} + C_{(s)} \rightarrow 2Pb_{(s)} + CO_2{(g)}$$

◆ In a **reversible** reaction the products can react to form the reactants, for example:

$$\text{nitrogen} + \text{hydrogen} \rightleftharpoons \text{ammonia}$$
$$N_2{(g)} + 3H_2{(g)} \rightleftharpoons 2NH_3{(g)}$$

◆ **Thermal decomposition** is the breakdown of a compound when heated, for example:

$$\text{calcium carbonate} \rightarrow \text{calcium oxide} + \text{carbon dioxide}$$
$$CaCO_3{(s)} \rightarrow CaO_{(s)} + CO_2{(g)}$$

Balancing symbol equations

◆ The total mass of the product(s) of a chemical reaction is always equal to the total mass of the reactant(s).
◆ This is because the products of a chemical reaction are made up from exactly the same atoms as the reactants.
◆ Symbol chemical equations must, therefore, always be balanced.
◆ The total number of atoms of each element on the reactant(s) side of the equation must be equal to the total number of atoms of the same element on the product(s) side of the equation.
◆ For example, if asked to balance the following:

$$Fe_2O_3{(s)} + ...CO_{(g)} \rightarrow ...Fe_{(l)} + ...CO_2{(g)}$$

• there are 2 iron atoms in Fe_2, so 2 atoms of iron will be produced
• iron oxide has 3 atoms of oxygen, so 3 molecules of carbon monoxide are needed to reduce the iron oxide, forming 3 molecules of carbon dioxide

$$Fe_2O_3{(s)} + 3CO_{(g)} \rightarrow 2Fe_{(l)} + 3CO_2{(g)}$$

Quantitative chemistry

Key facts

♦ Atoms of different elements have different masses.
♦ **Relative atomic mass** (r.a.m. or A_r) is the mass of an atom of an element compared with the mass of a hydrogen atom. For example, the mass of one atom of oxygen is equivalent to the mass of 16 atoms of hydrogen, so the r.a.m. of O is 16.

Important ideas

Calculating reacting volumes

♦ When asked to calculate reacting volumes you are usually given the volume of the relative formula mass of the gas. This is usually $24\,000\,cm^3$ at room temperature.
♦ For example, calcium reacts with water to form hydrogen and calcium hydroxide:
$$Ca(g) + 2H_2O(l) \rightarrow H_2(g) + Ca(OH)_2(aq)$$
♦ In an experiment, $60\,cm^3$ of hydrogen were evolved in this reaction. To calculate the mass of calcium that reacted with water (r.a.m.s Ca = 40, H = 1, O = 16):
• r.a.m. of Ca = 40, so 40 g of Ca would produce $24\,000\,cm^3$ of hydrogen
• $60\,cm^3$ of hydrogen are therefore produced by
$$= \frac{60 \times 40}{24\,000} \text{ g of Ca}$$
$$= \frac{2400}{24\,000}$$
$$= 0.1 \text{ g of Ca}$$

Calculating the percentage of an element in a compound

♦ The percentage of an element in a compound is:
$$\frac{\text{r.a.m. of element} \times 100}{\text{r.f.m. of compound}}$$
♦ For example, when calculating the percentage of nitrogen in ammonia (r.a.m.s N = 14, H = 1):
$$\% \text{ of nitrogen} = \frac{\text{r.a.m. of N} \times 100}{\text{r.f.m. of NH}_3}$$
$$= \frac{14 \times 100}{(14 + 3)}$$
$$= \frac{1400}{17}$$
$$= 82.35\%$$

Calculating relative formula mass

♦ When asked to calculate an r.f.m., you are given the formula of the compound and all the r.a.m.s.
♦ For example, when calculating the r.f.m. (M_r) of iron oxide, Fe_2O_3 (r.a.m.s Fe = 56, O = 16):
add (2×56) to (3×16)
$$= 112 + 48$$
$$= 160$$

Calculating reacting masses

◆ To calculate the reacting mass, multiply the r.a.m. or the r.f.m. by the number of atoms/molecules of the substance in a balanced equation of the reaction.
◆ For example, iron is reduced by carbon monoxide in a blast furnace:

$$Fe_2O_3(s) + 3CO(g) \rightarrow 2Fe(l) + 3CO_2(g)$$

To calculate the mass of iron that could be obtained from 16 000 tonnes of iron oxide (Fe_2O_3) (r.a.m.s Fe = 56, O = 16):

• first calculate the r.f.m. of iron oxide
  = (2 × 56) + (3 × 16)
  = 160
• next calculate the proportion of iron in iron oxide
  $$= \frac{112}{160}$$
  = 0.7
• finally, multiply the proportion of iron in iron oxide by the mass of iron oxide
  = 0.7 × 16 000 tonnes
  = 11 200 tonnes

Calculating the formula of a compound from reacting masses

◆ This can be done by using the ratios of the reacting masses.
◆ For example, a sample of sodium oxide was analysed and found to contain 1.6 g of oxygen and 4.6 g of sodium. To calculate the formula of sodium oxide (r.a.m.s Na = 23, O = 16):

• divide each reacting mass by the r.a.m. of the atom
  For sodium $\frac{4.6}{23} = 0.2$

  For oxygen $\frac{1.6}{16} = 0.1$

• The ratio is therefore
  0.2 sodium : 0.1 oxygen
  = 2 Na : 1 O
• So the formula is Na_2O

✖ Beware

◆ In these calculations you only receive full marks if you show *all* your working.
◆ Most gaseous elements have two atoms per molecule, so the r.f.m. gives a volume of 24 000 cm^3, but the r.a.m. gives 12 000 cm^3.

Changes to the atmosphere

🔑 Key facts

Composition of the present-day atmosphere of Earth

◆ For the last 200 million years the atmosphere has been made up of:
  • about 80% nitrogen
  • about 20% oxygen
  • small amounts of carbon dioxide, water vapour and noble gases

Composition of the early atmosphere of Earth

◆ Billions of years ago the composition of the atmosphere was:
  • mainly carbon dioxide
  • water vapour
  • small amounts of methane and ammonia
  • little or no oxygen

💡 Important ideas

Effects of humans

◆ The release of carbon dioxide by burning the carbon locked up over hundreds of millions of years in fossil fuels increases the level of carbon dioxide in the atmosphere.

◆ This contributes to the greenhouse effect.

Effects of organisms

◆ When plants evolved, their photo-synthesis:
  • removed carbon dioxide from the atmosphere
  • added oxygen to the atmosphere

◆ Animals then evolved — their respiration, along with that of plants, used some of the oxygen and returned some of the carbon dioxide.

◆ When plants and animals died, much of the carbon dioxide they had absorbed became locked up as carbonates in sedimentary rocks and as carbon in fossil fuels.

◆ Denitrifying bacteria converted nitrates from minerals into atmospheric nitrogen.

Effects of adding oxygen

◆ The methane and ammonia in the atmosphere reacted with the oxygen to form nitrogen.

◆ The oxygen in the atmosphere resulted in the development of an ozone layer. This filters out harmful ultraviolet radiation from the sun.

What happened to the gases in the early atmosphere of the Earth?

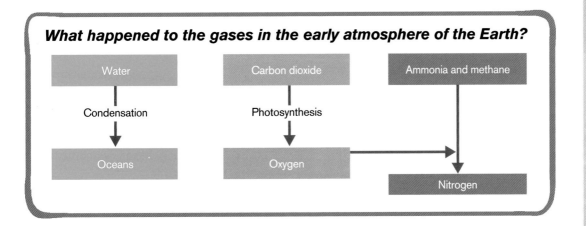

What happens to carbon dioxide?

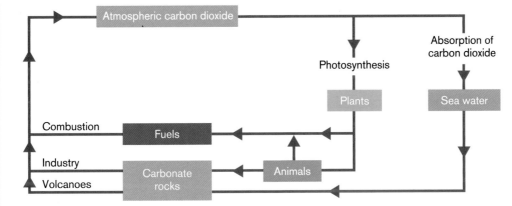

Effect of geological changes

◆ Carbonate rocks are sometimes moved deep into the Earth by geological activity. They may then release carbon dioxide back into the atmosphere via volcanoes.

Effect of sea water

◆ Carbon dioxide reacts with sea water, producing insoluble carbonates which are deposited as sediment and soluble hydrogencarbonates.

 **Beware**

◆ Do not confuse the ozone layer and the greenhouse effect.
◆ Revise photosynthesis, respiration and the carbon and nitrogen cycles from the biology section of this book — examiners will credit relevant points from biology.

Rocks

🔑 Key facts

Sedimentary rocks

◆ Sedimentary rocks are formed from layers of sediment deposited one on top of the other.

◆ The weight of the younger layers squeezes out water from the older ones.

◆ The sediment particles become compacted and cemented together by salts crystallising out of this water.

◆ This process often takes millions of years.

Igneous rocks

◆ Igneous rocks are formed from *molten rock* (magma).

◆ When molten rock is forced into the Earth's crust, **intrusive** igneous rocks (e.g. granites) are formed. The crystals in intrusive rocks are large and easily visible since the magma from which the rock was formed cooled slowly.

◆ When molten rock erupts from volcanoes it forms **extrusive** igneous rocks (e.g. basalt, volcanic ash). The crystals in extrusive rocks are small since the magma from which the rock was formed cooled quickly.

Metamorphic rocks

◆ Metamorphic rocks are formed by the action of *heat and pressure* on existing rocks.

◆ Movements of the Earth's crust may cause rocks to become buried deep under ground, where they are compressed and heated.

◆ This may change the texture and mineral structure of the rock, *without melting it* (e.g. slate and marble).

◆ Rocks composed of *interlocking crystals* are likely to be metamorphic (e.g. schist).

📈 Diagrams to remember

Exposed rocks can often be seen to be layered

These layers are the youngest – they were laid down after the older rocks were folded

These layers of rocks have been folded by forces in the crust

Folding

The layers of rocks here have been fractured (faulted) by forces in the Earth's crust

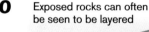

Faulting

The rock cycle

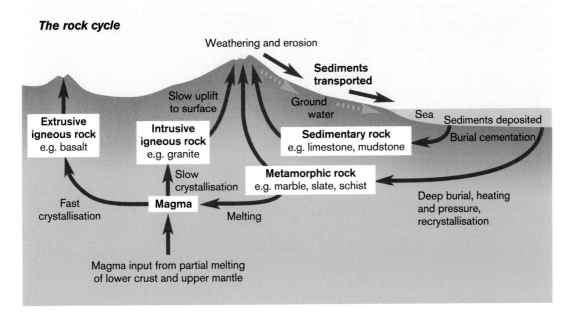

Weathering and erosion

Sediments transported

Slow uplift to surface

Ground water

Sea   Sediments deposited

Extrusive igneous rock e.g. basalt

Intrusive igneous rock e.g. granite

Sedimentary rock e.g. limestone, mudstone

Burial cementation

Slow crystallisation

Metamorphic rock e.g. marble, slate, schist

Fast crystallisation

Magma

Melting

Deep burial, heating and pressure, recrystallisation

Magma input from partial melting of lower crust and upper mantle

Important idea

The rock record

◆ Sedimentary rocks sometimes contain fossils.

◆ Fossils can be used to identify rocks in different layers and to decide which rocks are younger or older than others.

◆ Metamorphic rocks are associated with present-day and ancient mountain belts. They are evidence of the high temperatures and pressure created by mountain-building processes.

◆ At the surface of the Earth, younger sedimentary rocks usually lie on top of older rocks.

◆ Sedimentary rock layers are often found tilted, folded, fractured (faulted) and sometimes even turned upside down. This shows that the Earth's crust is unstable and has been subjected to very large forces.

◆ Large-scale movements of the Earth's crust can cause mountain ranges to form very slowly over millions of years. These replace older mountain ranges worn down by weathering and erosion.

Tectonics

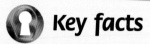

Key facts

What is meant by tectonics?

◆ The Earth's crust is cracked into a number of large pieces (tectonic plates).

◆ These plates are constantly moving at relative speeds of a few centimetres per year.

◆ The movement is the result of convection currents within the Earth's mantle, driven by heat released by natural radioactive processes.

Evidence for the tectonic theory

◆ The edges of land masses (continents) which are separated by thousands of kilometres of ocean (e.g. the east coast of South America and the west coast of Africa):
 • have shapes that fit quite closely
 • have similar patterns of rocks and fossils

◆ This suggests that they were once part of a single land mass which has split and been moved apart.

Diagrams to remember

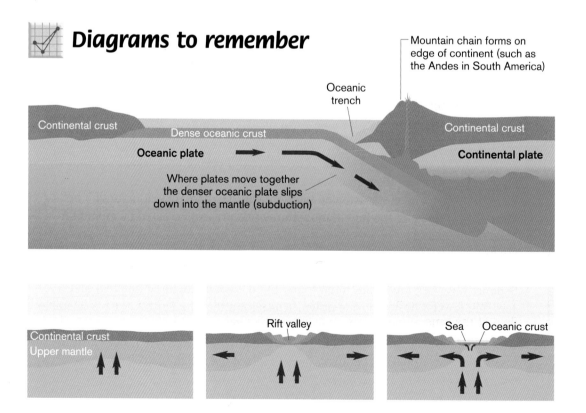

Mountain chain forms on edge of continent (such as the Andes in South America)

Oceanic trench

Continental crust

Dense oceanic crust

Oceanic plate

Continental crust

Continental plate

Where plates move together the denser oceanic plate slips down into the mantle (subduction)

Continental crust
Upper mantle

Rift valley

Sea   Oceanic crust

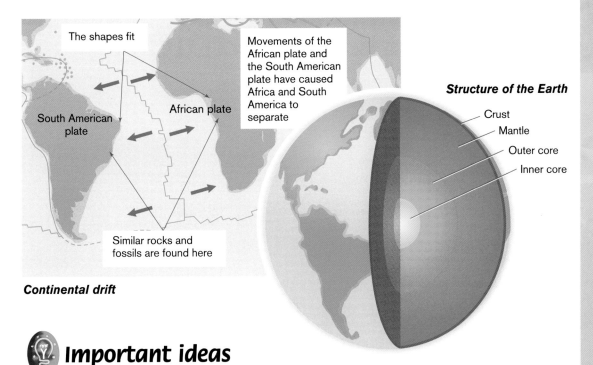

The shapes fit

Movements of the African plate and the South American plate have caused Africa and South America to separate

South American plate

African plate

Similar rocks and fossils are found here

Continental drift

Structure of the Earth

Crust
Mantle
Outer core
Inner core

Important ideas

Destructive margins

- ◆ When plates move towards each other they form destructive margins.
- ◆ As this happens, a thinner, denser **oceanic** plate can be driven down (subducted) beneath a thicker granitic **continental** plate, where it partially melts.
- ◆ The continental crust is compressed, causing folding, faulting and metamorphism.
- ◆ Earthquakes are produced and **magma** may rise through the continental crust to form volcanoes.
- ◆ This is happening along the western side of South America (the Andes).

Constructive margins

- ◆ When plates move apart they form constructive margins.
- ◆ This causes fractures which are filled by **magma**, producing new, basaltic, oceanic crust.
- ◆ This is known as sea-floor spreading and is happening along oceanic ridges, including the mid-Atlantic ridge.
- ◆ The iron-rich minerals in the magma record the direction of the Earth's magnetic field at the time when the rising magma solidified.
- ◆ Magnetic reversal patterns in oceanic crust occur in stripes parallel to oceanic ridges, matching the periodic reversals of the Earth's magnetic field and so supporting the concept of sea-floor spreading.

The periodic table

Group

1	2											3	4	5	6	7	0
							H 1										He 2
Li 3	Be 4											B 5	C 6	N 7	O 8	F 9	Ne 10
Na 11	Mg 12											Al 13	Si 14	P 15	S 16	Cl 17	Ar 18
K 19	Ca 20	Sc 21	Ti 22	V 23	Cr 24	Mn 25	Fe 26	Co 27	Ni 28	Cu 29	Zn 30	Ga 31	Ge 32	As 33	Se 34	Br 35	Kr 36
Rb 37	Sr 38	Y 39	Zr 40	Nb 41	Mo 42	Tc 43	Ru 44	Rh 45	Pd 46	Ag 47	Cd 48	In 49	Sn 50	Sb 51	Te 52	I 53	Xe 54

- the numbers are the **atomic numbers** of the elements
- the elements are **arranged in order of their atomic numbers**
- elements with similar properties are arranged in columns called **groups**
- the purple elements in groups 1 and 2 are **metals**
- the yellow shaded elements are metalloids
- the pink elements between group 2 and the metalloids are **transition metals**
- the green elements to the right of the metalloids are **non-metals**

 Important ideas

The periodic table and electrons

- ◆ The periodic table can be seen as an arrangement of the elements in terms of their electronic structure.
- ◆ From left to right, across each horizontal row (period) of the periodic table, a particular energy level is gradually filled up with electrons.
- ◆ In the next period, the next energy level is filled with electrons.
- ◆ Elements in the same group have similar properties because they have the same number of electrons in the highest occupied (outer) energy level.

Mendeleev's table

- ◆ Be prepared to be given earlier periodic tables such as that of Mendeleev (1869).
- ◆ You will be asked for differences between these and the modern periodic table.
  * Indicates gaps that Mendeleev left in his table for elements he thought would exist, but had yet to be discovered.

	Group 1	Group 2	Group 3	Group 4	Group 5	Group 6	Group 7
Period 1	H						
Period 2	Li	Be	B	C	N	O	F
Period 3	Na	Mg	Al	Si	P	S	Cl
Period 4	K Cu	Ca Zn	* *	Ti *	V As	Cr Se	Mn Br
Period 5	Rb Ag	Sr Cd	Y In	Zr Sn	Nb Sb	Mo Te	* I

🔑 Key facts

Group 1: the alkali metals

◆ The alkali metals:
- are metals with a low density
- react with non-metals to form ionic compounds in which the metal ion carries a +1 charge (these compounds are white solids which dissolve in water to form colourless solutions)
- react with water, releasing hydrogen
- form hydroxides which dissolve in water to give alkaline solutions

◆ The further down group 1 an element is, the lower its melting and boiling points.

◆ The higher the energy level of the outer electrons in the elements in group 1, the *more easily electrons are lost*, so *reactivity increases down the group*.

Group 7: the halogens

◆ The halogens:
- have coloured vapours
- consist of molecules which are made up of pairs of atoms
- form ionic salts with metals in which the chloride, bromide or iodide ion (halide ions) carries a –1 charge

◆ A more reactive halogen can displace a less reactive halogen from an aqueous solution of its salt.

◆ The further down group 7 an element is, the higher its melting and boiling points.

◆ The higher the energy level of outer electrons of the elements in group 7 the *less easily electrons are gained*, so *reactivity decreases down the group*.

Group 0: the noble gases

◆ The noble gases:
- are all chemically very unreactive
- exist as individual atoms rather than as diatomic gases (like most other gaseous elements)
- are used as inert gases in filament lamps and in electrical discharge tubes

◆ The first element in the group, helium, is much less dense than air and is used in balloons.

◆ Noble gases are unreactive and monatomic because their highest occupied energy level is full — the atoms have no tendency to gain, lose or share electrons.

❌ Beware

◆ Don't mix up reactivity in groups 1 and 7:
- in group 1, reactivity increases down the group because the bigger the atom, the more easily outer electrons are lost
- in group 7, reactivity decreases down the group because the bigger the atom, the less easily outer electrons are gained

Non-metals, metals, acids and alkalis

🔑 Key facts

Properties of non-metals
- Non-metals usually have low melting points and boiling points (at room temperature all the group 0 elements are gases, the first two group 7 elements are gases and the third, bromine, is a liquid).
- They are mostly brittle and crumbly when solid.
- They are mostly poor conductors of heat and electricity.

Properties of metals
- Metals are good conductors of heat and electricity.
- They can easily be bent or hammered into shape.
- They have high melting points (except for mercury, which is a liquid at room temperature).

Reactivity series
- Some metals are more reactive than others.
- By observing how various metals react:
  - with air, to produce metal oxides
  - with water (cold, hot or as steam) to produce metal hydroxides (or oxides) and hydrogen
  - with dilute acids, to produce metal salts and hydrogen

  they can be arranged in a reactivity series. The most reactive metals are at the top of the series and the least reactive at the bottom.

Transition metals
- In the centre of the periodic table is a block of metallic elements. These elements are known as transition metals.
- Compared with other metals, transition metals:
  - are hard, tough and strong
  - are much less reactive and so do not react (corrode) so quickly with oxygen and/or water
- These properties make transition metals very useful as structural materials.
- Most transition metals form coloured compounds. These can be seen:
  - in pottery glazes of various colours
  - in weathered copper (green)
- Many transition metals, including iron and nickel, are used as catalysts.

Acids and alkalis
- When a substance dissolves in water it forms an aqueous solution which may be acidic, alkaline or neutral.
- Water itself is neutral.
- Indicators can be used to show whether a solution is acidic, alkaline or neutral by the way their colours change.
- The pH scale is used to show how acidic or alkaline a solution is:

$$0 \longleftarrow\!\!\!\!-\!\!\!-\!\!\!- 7 \longrightarrow 14$$

| increasing acidity | neutral | increasing alkalinity |

Compounds of alkali metals

◆ Sodium chloride (common salt) is a compound of an alkali metal and a halogen.
◆ The electrolysis of sodium chloride solution (brine) is an important industrial process:
  • chlorine gas is formed at the positive electrode
  • hydrogen gas is formed at the negative electrode
  • a solution of sodium hydroxide is also formed

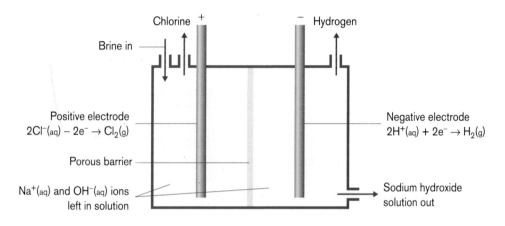

Chlorine + − Hydrogen

Brine in

Positive electrode
$2Cl^-(aq) - 2e^- \rightarrow Cl_2(g)$

Negative electrode
$2H^+(aq) + 2e^- \rightarrow H_2(g)$

Porous barrier

$Na^+(aq)$ and $OH^-(aq)$ ions left in solution

Sodium hydroxide solution out

◆ Each of these products can be used to make other useful materials:
  • chlorine is used to kill bacteria in drinking water and in swimming pools, and to manufacture hydrochloric acid, disinfectants, bleach and the plastic (polymer) known as PVC
  • hydrogen is used in the manufacture of ammonia and margarine
  • sodium hydroxide is used in the manufacture of soap, paper and ceramics
◆ Silver chloride, silver bromide and silver iodide (silver halides) are reduced to silver by the action of light, X-rays and radiation from radioactive substances. They are used to make photographic film and photographic paper.
◆ Hydrogen halides are gases which dissolve in water to produce acidic solutions.
◆ Compounds of alkali metals, called salts, can be made by reacting solutions of their hydroxides, which are alkaline, with acids. In these neutralisation reactions:
  acid + alkaline hydroxide solution → a neutral salt solution + water
◆ The particular salt produced in any reaction between an alkali and an acid depends on:
  • the metal in the alkali
  • the acid used
◆ Neutralising hydrochloric acid produces chlorides.
◆ Neutralising nitric acid produces nitrates.
◆ Neutralising sulphuric acid produces sulphates.

Rates of reactions and enzymes

🔑 Key facts

Activation energy
- Chemical reactions can only occur when reacting particles collide with each other and with sufficient energy.
- The minimum amount of energy particles must have to react is the activation energy.

The effect of temperature
- Increasing the temperature increases the speed of the reacting particles so that they collide more frequently and more energetically.
- This increases the rate of reaction.

The effect of concentration of reactants
- Increasing the concentration of reactants in solutions increases the frequency of collisions.
- This increases the rate of reaction.

The effect of pressure
- Increasing the pressure of reacting gases increases the frequency of collisions.
- This increases the rate of reaction.

The effect of surface area of reactants
- A powdered reactant has a total surface area greater than that of a lump of the same mass.
- Increasing the surface area increases the frequency of collisions.
- This increases the rate of reaction.

The effect of catalysts
- A catalyst increases the rate of a chemical reaction but is not used up during the reaction.
- It is used over and over again to speed up the conversion of reactants to products.
- Different reactions need different catalysts.
- A catalyst lowers the activation energy of a reaction.

Enzymes
- The chemical reactions brought about by living cells are quite fast in conditions that are warm rather than hot.
- This is because the cells use catalysts called enzymes.
- Enzymes are protein molecules which are usually damaged by temperatures above about 45°C.
- Different enzymes work best at different pH values.

Important ideas

Fermentation
◆ Living cells use chemical reactions to produce new materials.
◆ Yeast cells convert sugar into carbon dioxide and alcohol.
◆ This process is called fermentation and is used to produce the alcohol in beer and wine and the bubbles of carbon dioxide that make bread dough rise.

Yoghurt manufacture
◆ Bacteria are used to produce yoghurt from milk.
◆ The bacteria convert the sugar in milk (lactose) to lactic acid.

Diagrams to remember

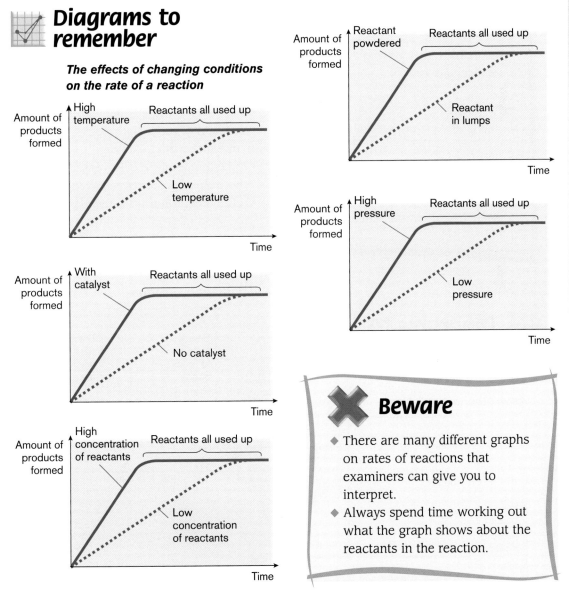

The effects of changing conditions on the rate of a reaction

Amount of products formed — High temperature — Reactants all used up — Low temperature — Time

Amount of products formed — With catalyst — Reactants all used up — No catalyst — Time

Amount of products formed — High concentration of reactants — Reactants all used up — Low concentration of reactants — Time

Amount of products formed — Reactant powdered — Reactants all used up — Reactant in lumps — Time

Amount of products formed — High pressure — Reactants all used up — Low pressure — Time

✖ Beware

◆ There are many different graphs on rates of reactions that examiners can give you to interpret.
◆ Always spend time working out what the graph shows about the reactants in the reaction.

Reversible reactions and energy in reactions

🔑 Key facts

Reversible reactions

- In some chemical reactions, the products of the reaction can react to produce the original reactants.
- Such reactions are called **reversible** reactions and are represented as:

$$A + B \rightleftharpoons C$$

- For example:

nitrogen + hydrogen $\rightleftharpoons$ ammonia

Equilibrium

- When a reversible reaction occurs in a closed system, an equilibrium is reached when the reaction occurs at exactly the same rate in each direction.
- The relative amounts of the reacting substances at equilibrium depend on the conditions of the reaction.
- In an **endothermic** reaction:
  - if the temperature is increased, the yield of products is increased
  - if the temperature is decreased, the yield of products is decreased
- In an **exothermic** reaction:
  - if the temperature is increased, the yield of products is decreased
  - if the temperature is decreased, the yield of products is increased

📈 Diagrams to remember

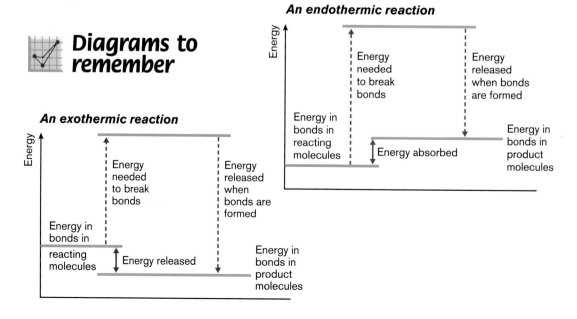

An endothermic reaction

Energy

Energy needed to break bonds

Energy released when bonds are formed

Energy in bonds in reacting molecules

Energy absorbed

Energy in bonds in product molecules

An exothermic reaction

Energy

Energy needed to break bonds

Energy released when bonds are formed

Energy in bonds in reacting molecules

Energy released

Energy in bonds in product molecules

Important ideas

Bond energy calculations

◆ First add up the total energy involved in breaking the bonds on the left-hand side of the equation.
◆ Then add up the total energy involved in forming new bonds on the right-hand side of the equation.
◆ For example, the following symbol equation shows the reaction between methane and oxygen:

$$CH_4 + 2O_2 \rightarrow CO_2 + 2H_2O$$

◆ The structural formulae below show the bonds in each molecule involved:

$$H-\underset{\underset{H}{|}}{\overset{\overset{H}{|}}{C}}-H + 2[O=O] \longrightarrow O=C=O + 2[H-O-H]$$

◆ The table below gives the energy of the bonds:

Bond	Bond energy (kJ per mol)
C–H	413
C=O	805
O=O	498
O–H	464

◆ To calculate the energy released when the relative formula mass of methane is completely oxidised:
  • energy needed to break bonds
    = (4 × C–H bonds) + (2 × O=O bonds)
    = (4 × 413) + (2 × 498)
    = 2648 kJ
  • energy released in forming bonds
    = (2 × C=O bonds) + (4 × O–H bonds)
    = (2 × 805) + (4 × 464)
    = 3466 kJ
  • net energy released = (3466 kJ – 2648 kJ)
    = +818 kJ
◆ In **exothermic** reactions the energy released when new bonds are formed is greater than that needed to break existing bonds.
◆ Since the energy change has a *positive* value, the reaction is **exothermic**.

Exothermic and endothermic reactions

◆ An exothermic reaction is one that transfers energy, often as heat, to the surroundings.
◆ An endothermic reaction is one that takes in energy, often as heat, from the surroundings.
◆ If a reversible reaction is exothermic in one direction, it is endothermic in the opposite direction. The same amount of energy is transferred in both directions.

 **Beware**

◆ Don't confuse rate of reaction with the concentration of substances in the equilibrium mixture.
◆ Don't forget to state whether the net energy change is positive or negative in bond energy calculations.

physics

Circuits

Key facts

- A **current** will flow through an electrical component only if there is a **potential difference (p.d.)** across it.
- **p.d.** is measured in **volts (V)** using a voltmeter connected *across* a component.
- **Current** is measured in **amperes (A)** using an ammeter connected *in series* with a component.
- Components **resist** the flow of currents.
- **Resistance** is measured in **ohms (Ω)**.
- The bigger the resistance, the smaller the current produced by a particular p.d.

- In series circuits:
  - the total resistance is the sum of the separate resistances
  - the same current flows through each component
  - the total p.d. of the supply is shared between the components

- In parallel circuits:
  - the same p.d. occurs across each component
  - the current through each component depends on its resistance
  - the total current in the circuit is the sum of the currents through the separate components

Diagrams to remember

Circuit symbols

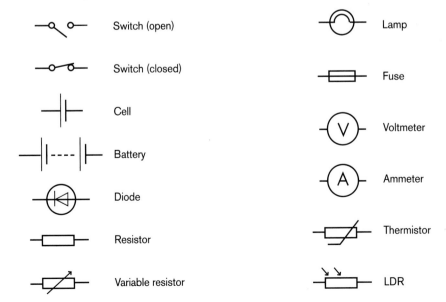

Switch (open)		Lamp	
Switch (closed)		Fuse	
Cell		Voltmeter	
Battery		Ammeter	
Diode		Thermistor	
Resistor		LDR	
Variable resistor			

 **Important ideas**

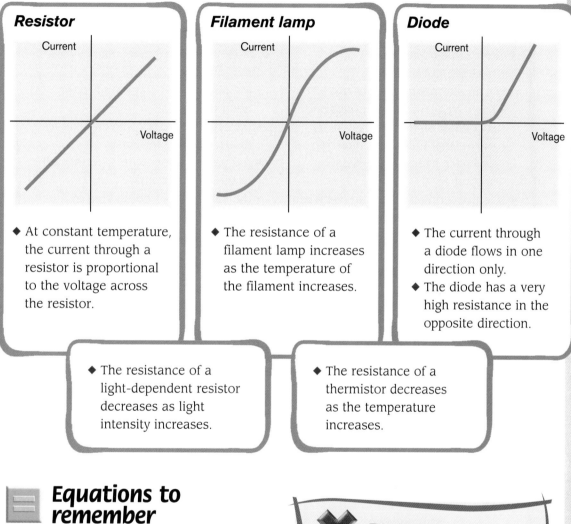

Resistor

Current

Voltage

♦ At constant temperature, the current through a resistor is proportional to the voltage across the resistor.

Filament lamp

Current

Voltage

♦ The resistance of a filament lamp increases as the temperature of the filament increases.

Diode

Current

Voltage

♦ The current through a diode flows in one direction only.
♦ The diode has a very high resistance in the opposite direction.

♦ The resistance of a light-dependent resistor decreases as light intensity increases.

♦ The resistance of a thermistor decreases as the temperature increases.

Equations to remember

♦ Make sure you know the three versions of the Ohm's law equation:

$$\Omega = \frac{V}{A}$$

$$V = \Omega \times A$$

$$A = \frac{V}{\Omega}$$

Beware

♦ Don't confuse current and voltage.
♦ Don't confuse series and parallel.
♦ Don't confuse current, voltage and resistance in series and parallel circuits.

Mains electricity

🔑 Key facts

The mains supply
◆ The UK mains supply:
  • is about 230 volts
  • is an alternating current (a.c.)
  • has a frequency of 50 cycles per second or 50 hertz (Hz), which means that it changes direction and back again 50 times each second
◆ The live terminal alternates between a positive and negative voltage with respect to the neutral terminal.
◆ The neutral terminal stays at a voltage close to zero with respect to Earth.

The three-pin plug
◆ When connecting an appliance to a three-pin plug:
  • the blue wire is connected to the neutral terminal
  • the brown wire is connected via a fuse to the live terminal
  • the green/yellow wire is connected to the earth terminal
  • the cable should be secured in the plug by the cable grip
  • a fuse of the correct value (rating) should be in place

💡 Important ideas

Safety measures
◆ Appliances with metal cases need to be earthed.
◆ If a fault in the appliance connects the case to the live wire, a very large current flows to earth and overloads the fuse.
◆ When the current through a fuse wire is too high, the wire becomes hot and melts, breaking the circuit and switching off the current.

Power
◆ As an electric current flows through a circuit, energy is transferred from the power supply to the components in the electrical circuit.
◆ How much electrical energy an appliance transfers depends on:
  • how long the appliance is switched on
  • how fast the appliance transfers energy (its power)
◆ The power of an appliance is measured in watts (W) or kilowatts (kW).
◆ 1 watt is the transfer of 1 J of energy in 1 second.
◆ 1 kW = 1000 W
◆ The amount of energy transferred from the mains is measured in kilowatt hours, called Units.

Equations to remember

- ◆ Rate of energy transfer:

  power = potential difference × current
  (watt, W)   (volt, V)   (ampere, A)

- ◆ The cost of electricity:

  energy transferred   =   power   ×   time
  (kilowatt hour, kWh)   (kilowatt, kW)   (hour, h)

  total cost of energy = number of Units × cost per Unit

- ◆ The total amount of energy transferred:

  energy transferred   =   power   ×   time
  (joule, J)   (watt, W)   (second, s)

✖ Beware

- ◆ In calculating energy transfer, don't forget to:
  - convert the power of the device into kW, for example 500 W = 0.5 kW
  - convert time into hours, for example 15 minutes = 0.25 hours

- ◆ Make sure you can label a three-pin plug:

Case insulator
Green/yellow wire
Blue wire
Neutral pin

Earth pin
Fuse
Brown wire
Live pin
Cable grip

- ◆ Make sure you can read diagrams of electric meters.
  You might be given an illustration of two meter readings and asked to calculate the number of kilowatt hours or the number of Units of electrical energy used. Note that the right-hand number is in tenths of a kWh.

kWh
0 6 4 7 1 5 ↑
10000 1000 100 10 1 $\frac{1}{10}$

kWh
0 7 1 9 8 5 ↑
10000 1000 100 10 1 $\frac{1}{10}$

7198.5
− 6471.5
727.0
i.e. 727 kWh
or Units

Charge

Key facts

Electrostatics

◆ When certain different materials are rubbed against each other they become electrically charged.

◆ Electrons, which have a negative charge, are rubbed off one material onto the other.

◆ The material that gains electrons becomes negatively charged.

◆ The material that loses electrons is left with an equal positive charge.

◆ Electrically charged objects attract small objects placed near to them.

◆ Like-charged objects repel each other.

◆ Opposite-charged objects attract each other.

When the ruler is rubbed with the duster, it becomes negatively charged because electrons are rubbed off the duster onto the ruler

Charge and current

◆ In solid conductors, an electric current is a flow of electrons.

◆ Metals are good conductors of electricity because some of the electrons from their atoms can move freely throughout the metal structure.

Charge in circuits

◆ An electric current is a flow of charge.

◆ The higher the voltage of a supply, the greater the amount of energy transferred for a given amount of charge that flows.

◆ When electrical charge flows through a resistor, electrical energy is transferred as heat.

Discharge

◆ The greater the charge on an isolated object, the greater the potential difference between the object and the Earth.

◆ If the voltage becomes high enough, a spark may jump across the gap between the object and any earthed conductor that is brought near it.

◆ A charged conductor can be discharged by connecting it to Earth with a conductor.

Equations to remember

$$\begin{array}{ccccc} \text{energy transferred} & = & \text{potential difference} & \times & \text{charge} \\ \text{(joule, J)} & & \text{(volt, V)} & & \text{(coulomb, C)} \end{array}$$

$$\begin{array}{ccccc} \text{charge} & = & \text{current} & \times & \text{time} \\ \text{(coulomb, C)} & & \text{(ampere, A)} & & \text{(second, s)} \end{array}$$

Diagram to remember

Positive electrode (anode)
+

Negative electrode (cathode)
−

Negatively charged ions (anions)

Positively charged ions (cations)

Electrolyte

Electrolysis

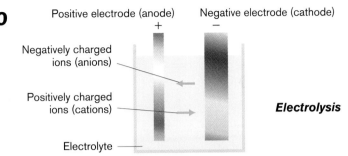

Important ideas

Using electrostatics

◆ Industrial paint sprayers are a good example of using electrostatics.
◆ The paint droplets are all given a positive charge as they leave the nozzle.
◆ Because like charges repel, the charged paint droplets separate into a fine spray.
◆ The object to be painted (e.g. a car door) is given a negative charge. This attracts the positively charged paint droplets.

Nozzle

Car door

Electrolysis

◆ When some chemical compounds are melted or dissolved in water they conduct electricity.
◆ These compounds are made up of electrically charged particles called ions.
◆ The current is due to negatively charged ions moving to the positive terminal (electrode).
◆ The positively charged ions move to the negative electrode.
◆ Uncharged substances are released at the electrodes. This process is called **electrolysis**.
◆ During electrolysis the mass and/or volume of the substance deposited or released at the electrode increases:
  • as the current increases
  • when the time for which the current flows increases

Beware

◆ It is advisable to revise ions and the giant structure of metals as you revise this section.
◆ Most specifications require you to describe:
  • one use of electrostatics, for example in a photocopier or paint spray
  • one danger of electrostatics, for example the dangerous build-up of charge when refuelling aircraft

Electromagnetic forces

Key facts

Magnets

◆ If a magnet is free to move, it comes to rest pointing in a north–south direction.

◆ The end of a magnet that points north (or south) is called the north- (or south-) seeking pole.

◆ A magnet produces a magnetic field.

◆ A magnet exerts a force on any piece of magnetic material.

◆ Like poles repel.

◆ Unlike poles attract.

Diagrams to remember

Magnetic field pattern

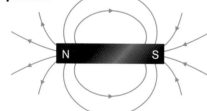

Magnetic forces

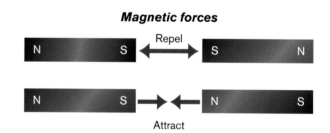

Important ideas

Electromagnets

◆ A coil of wire acts like a bar magnet when an electric current flows through it. This is called an **electromagnet**.

◆ The strength of an electromagnet can be increased by:
  • placing an iron core inside the coil
  • increasing the number of turns on the coil
  • increasing the size of the current flowing through the coil

◆ Reversing the current in an electromagnet reverses the poles of the electromagnet.

The motor effect

◆ When a wire carrying an electric current is placed in a magnetic field, it experiences a force.

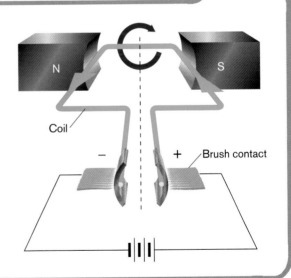

Current

Field

Movement

Wire

◆ The size of the force can be increased by:
  • increasing the strength of the magnetic field
  • increasing the size of the current
◆ The direction of the force is reversed if either the direction of the current or the direction of the magnetic field is reversed.

The electric motor

◆ The electric motor shown has:
  • a permanent magnet
  • a coil through which a current is passed
◆ The magnetic field exerts a force on the coil, causing it to rotate.
◆ The size of the force on the coil can be increased by:
  • increasing the strength of the magnet
  • increasing the size of the current
  • increasing the number of turns on the coil

N   S

Coil

–   +   Brush contact

Beware

◆ Electromagnets have many uses in household devices, including loudspeakers and many circuit breakers and locks.
◆ You will probably not have seen the particular device in a question before.
◆ Work out from the diagram:
  • which part will move when the current flows through the coil
  • whether or not this movement will break the circuit

Electromagnetic induction

Key facts

Induction

◆ If a magnet is moved into a coil of wire that is part of a complete circuit, a current is produced (**induced**) in the wire.

◆ If the magnet is moved out of the coil, or the other pole of the magnet is moved into the coil, the direction of the induced current is reversed.

◆ A current is induced only if the coil or the magnet is moving.

Diagrams to remember

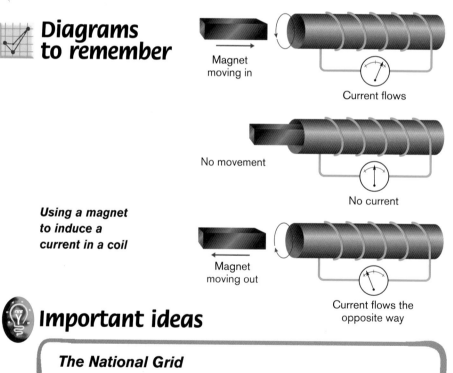

Magnet moving in

Current flows

No movement

No current

Using a magnet to induce a current in a coil

Magnet moving out

Current flows the opposite way

Important ideas

The National Grid

◆ At power stations, transformers are used to produce very high voltages before the electricity is transmitted to where it is needed through power lines (the National Grid).

◆ The higher the voltage, the smaller the current needed to transmit energy at the same rate. Therefore less energy is wasted by heating up the power lines.

Generators

◆ Electricity can be generated by rotating a coil of wire in a magnetic field or by rotating a magnet inside a coil of wire.

◆ If a wire, or coil of wire, 'cuts through' a magnetic field, or vice-versa, a voltage (potential difference) is produced between the ends of the wire.

◆ The size of the induced voltage increases when:
  • the speed of the movement increases
  • the strength of the magnetic field is increased
  • the number of turns on the coil is increased
  • the area of the coil is increased

a.c. generator (alternator or dynamo)

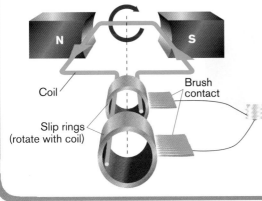

Transformers

◆ A changing magnetic field will produce an induced voltage in a coil. This is how a transformer works.

◆ Transformers are used to change the voltage of an a.c. supply.

◆ A transformer consists of two separate coils wound around an iron core.

◆ When an alternating voltage is applied across one coil (the primary), an alternating voltage is produced across the other coil (secondary).

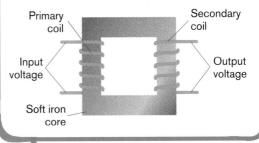

Equation to remember

The voltages across the primary and secondary coils of a transformer are related as shown:

$$\frac{\text{voltage across primary (volt, V)}}{\text{voltage across secondary (volt, V)}} = \frac{\text{number of turns on primary}}{\text{number of turns on secondary}}$$

You will always be given three of the values for the formula, so practise rearranging the formula to give each of the four values.

✖ Beware

◆ Remember that a voltage is only induced when something moves — a wire, or a coil, or a magnet.

◆ Changing the direction of movement changes the direction of the current.

◆ Transformers only work on a.c., where the direction of the current changes 50 times per second.

Forces and motion

🔑 Key facts

- The steeper the slope of a distance–time graph, the greater the speed.
- The velocity of an object is its speed in a given direction.
- Acceleration is the rate at which velocity changes.
- The steeper the slope of a velocity–time graph, the greater the acceleration.

📈 Diagrams to remember

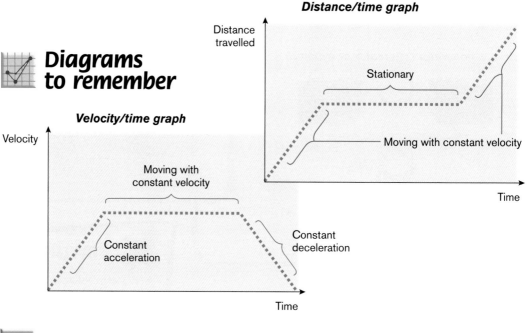

Velocity/time graph

Distance/time graph

＝ Equations to remember

$$\text{speed (metre per second, m/s)} = \frac{\text{distance travelled (metre, m)}}{\text{time taken (second, s)}}$$

$$\text{acceleration (metre per second, m/s}^2\text{)} = \frac{\text{change in velocity (metre per second, m/s)}}{\text{time taken for change (second, s)}}$$

Important ideas

Using graphs in calculations

♦ In distance–time graphs:
- the gradient gives the speed of an object
- the steeper the slope, the greater the speed

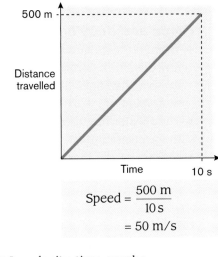

500 m

Distance travelled

Time   10 s

$$\text{Speed} = \frac{500 \text{ m}}{10 \text{ s}}$$
$$= 50 \text{ m/s}$$

♦ In velocity–time graphs:
- the gradient represents acceleration

- the steeper the slope of the graph, the greater the acceleration
- the area under the graph represents the distance travelled

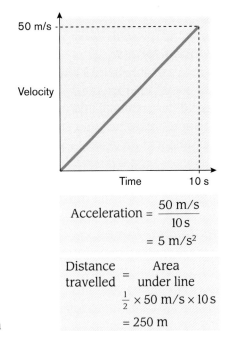

50 m/s

Velocity

Time   10 s

$$\text{Acceleration} = \frac{50 \text{ m/s}}{10 \text{ s}}$$
$$= 5 \text{ m/s}^2$$

$$\frac{\text{Distance}}{\text{travelled}} = \frac{\text{Area}}{\text{under line}}$$
$$\frac{1}{2} \times 50 \text{ m/s} \times 10 \text{ s}$$
$$= 250 \text{ m}$$

Other illustrations of velocity

♦ You might be given data about movement in other forms, for example drawings of punched ticker-tape, or of oil drops from a vehicle on a road.

W   X   Y   Z

♦ In this diagram of oil drops, the vehicle is decelerating between W and X, travelling at constant velocity between X and Y, and accelerating between Y and Z.

✖ Beware

- Speed and velocity are *not* the same.
- Don't confuse the units — speed is m/s, acceleration is m/s^2.
- The gradient of a distance–time graph indicates speed, the gradient of a velocity–time graph indicates acceleration.
- If an object is slowing down, its acceleration has a negative value.

Forces, acceleration and friction

🔑 Key facts

Balanced forces

◆ In the case of balanced forces, when two bodies interact, the forces on each other are equal and opposite.

◆ Balanced forces have no effect on the movement of an object. It will remain stationary or, if it is already moving, it will continue to move at the *same speed* and in the *same direction*.

Unbalanced forces

◆ If the forces acting on an object do not cancel each other out, an unbalanced force will act on the object.

◆ This unbalanced force will affect the movement of the object.

◆ How the movement is affected depends on the direction and the size of the unbalanced force:
  • a stationary object will start to move in the direction of the unbalanced force
  • an object moving in the direction of the force will speed up
  • an object moving in the opposite direction from the force will slow down

• the greater the size of the unbalanced force, the faster the object will speed up or slow down

Force and acceleration

◆ When an unbalanced force acts on an object in a particular direction, its speed changes (it accelerates) in that direction.

◆ The greater the force, the greater the acceleration.

◆ The bigger the mass of an object, the greater the force needed to give the object a particular acceleration.

Friction

◆ A force of friction acts:
  • when an object moves through air or a liquid
  • when solid surfaces slide across each other

◆ The direction of this force of friction is always opposite from the direction in which the object or surface is moving.

◆ When a vehicle has a steady speed, the frictional forces balance the driving force.

✅ Diagrams to remember

Opposing forces

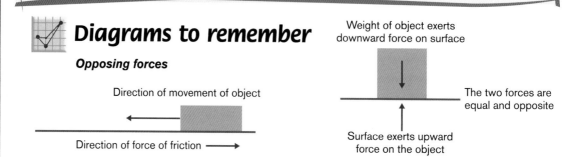

Direction of movement of object

Direction of force of friction ⟶

Weight of object exerts downward force on surface

The two forces are equal and opposite

Surface exerts upward force on the object

Important ideas

Terminal velocity

◆ The faster an object moves through a gas or a liquid (a fluid), the greater the force of friction that acts on it.
◆ When a body falls:
  • initially it accelerates due to the force of gravity
  • frictional forces increase until they balance the gravitational forces
  • the resultant force eventually reaches zero and the body falls at its terminal velocity

Stopping distance

◆ The greater the speed of a vehicle:
  • the greater the braking force needed to stop it in a certain distance
  • the greater the distance needed to stop it with a certain braking force
◆ The stopping distance of a vehicle depends on:
  • the distance the vehicle travels during the driver's reaction time
  • the distance the vehicle travels under the braking force

Equation to remember

One newton is the force needed to give a mass of one kilogram an acceleration of one metre per second squared:

force	=	mass	×	acceleration
(newtons, N)		(kilograms, kg)		(metres/second squared, m/s^2)

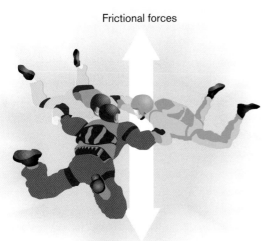

Frictional forces

Force of gravity

✖ Beware

◆ Don't confuse the direction of forces:
  • gravity acts in a downwards direction
  • weight acts in a downwards direction
  • friction acts in the opposite direction from the movement of the object
◆ If an object is moving at a constant velocity, then the forces acting on the object are balanced. There is *no net force* on the object.

Forces and pressure

🔑 Key facts

Stretching forces

◆ The greater the stretching force applied to a metal wire or spring, the greater the extension (stretch) produced.

◆ Provided the elastic limit is not exceeded, it returns to its original shape and size when the force is removed, i.e. it is **elastic**.

◆ If the **elastic limit** is exceeded, it remains permanently **deformed**.

Pressure

◆ The greater the force that acts on a certain area, the greater the pressure.

◆ The greater the area over which a force acts, the smaller the pressure.

◆ A pressure of 1 Pa is exerted by a force of 1 N acting at right angles to an area of 1 m^2.

◆ At any point in a liquid or gas the same pressure acts equally in all directions.

◆ The pressure in a fluid increases with depth.

📈 Diagrams to remember

Forces applied to a spring

Don't forget – it is the **extension** of the spring that is measured and plotted, *not* the length

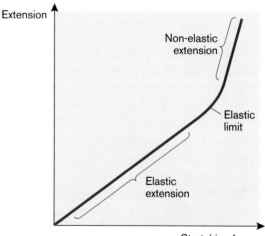

Elastic and non-elastic extension

Important ideas

The effect of pressure on gases
◆ When the pressure on a gas increases and its temperature stays the same, its volume decreases.
◆ For a fixed mass of gas at constant temperature, the *volume is inversely proportional to the pressure.*

Hydraulics
◆ Liquids can be used to send forces to where they are needed:
  • a force is applied to the liquid using a **master piston** which puts the liquid under pressure
  • the liquid then presses on a **slave piston** which exerts a force where it is needed

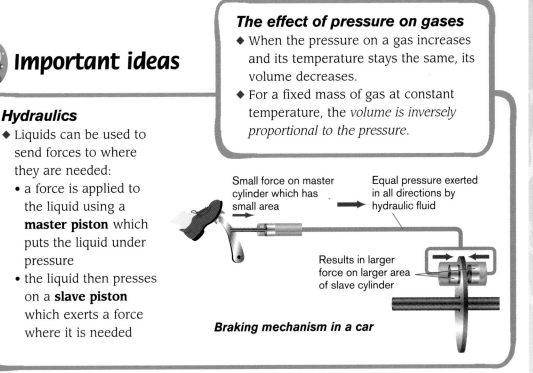

Small force on master cylinder which has small area

Equal pressure exerted in all directions by hydraulic fluid

Results in larger force on larger area of slave cylinder

Braking mechanism in a car

Equations to remember

$$\text{pressure (pascal, Pa)} = \frac{\text{force (newton, N)}}{\text{area (metre squared, m}^2)}$$

The pressure and volume of a fixed mass of gas at constant temperature are related:

initial pressure × initial volume = final pressure × final volume

✖ Beware

◆ Practise the gas equation — you will be given three of the values and asked to calculate the fourth, so make sure you can rearrange the formula.
◆ In a hydraulic system, the slave cylinder has a *larger* area than the master cylinder. Since there is the same pressure on both cylinders, the force on the slave cylinder will be the greater.

Waves

🔑 Key facts

Reflection

◆ Sounds bounce back (reflect) from hard surfaces as echoes.

◆ When a ray of light is reflected from a flat, shiny surface the angle at which it leaves the surface is the same as the angle at which it meets the surface.

◆ Waves travelling along a rope or spring, or travelling across the surface of water, can be reflected.

Refraction

◆ Light waves change direction (are refracted) when they cross the boundary between one transparent substance and another, unless they meet the boundary at right angles.

◆ Sound waves and waves travelling across the surface of water can also be refracted.

◆ The change in the speed of water waves when they cross the boundary between two different depths causes a change in their direction.

◆ Waves are refracted because they travel at *different speeds* in different substances.

✓ Diagrams to remember

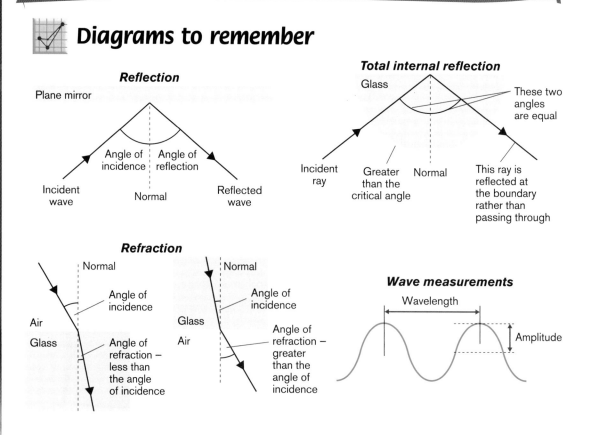

Reflection

Plane mirror

Angle of incidence | Angle of reflection

Incident wave

Normal

Reflected wave

Total internal reflection

Glass

These two angles are equal

Incident ray

Greater than the critical angle

Normal

This ray is reflected at the boundary rather than passing through

Refraction

Normal

Angle of incidence

Air

Glass

Angle of refraction – less than the angle of incidence

Normal

Angle of incidence

Glass

Air

Angle of refraction – greater than the angle of incidence

Wave measurements

Wavelength

Amplitude

Important ideas

Optical fibres

◆ When light travels down an optical fibre it stays inside the fibre until it emerges from the other end. This is because light travels down optical fibres by repeated total internal reflection.

Frequency, wavelength and amplitude

◆ When waves travel along ropes or springs or across the surface of water they set up regular patterns of disturbances.
◆ The maximum disturbance caused by a wave is called its **amplitude**.
◆ The distance between a particular point on one disturbance and the same point on the next is called the **wavelength**.
◆ The number of waves produced by a source (or passing a particular point) each second is called the **frequency**, and is measured in hertz (Hz).

Diffraction

◆ When a wave moves through a gap, or past an obstacle, it spreads out from the edges. This is called diffraction.
◆ Waves having a longer wavelength are more strongly diffracted.
◆ Because of diffraction:
  • sounds can sometimes be heard in the shadow of buildings
  • radio signals can sometimes be received in the shadow of hills

Transverse and longitudinal waves

◆ Waves transfer energy from a source to other places without any matter being transferred.
◆ The waves that travel along ropes and across the surface of water are **transverse** waves.
◆ In transverse waves the disturbances in the substance through which the waves travel is at right angles to the direction in which the waves themselves travel.
◆ Light waves are transverse waves and can travel through a vacuum, i.e. they do not need a medium.
◆ The waves that travel through springs may also be **longitudinal**.
◆ In longitudinal waves the disturbances in the spring are along the same direction as that in which the waves themselves travel.
◆ Sound waves travel through solids, liquids and gases as longitudinal waves.

✖ Beware

◆ Reflection, refraction and diffraction sound quite similar — don't confuse them.
◆ Compose a mnemonic to help you to remember whether light is refracted away from/towards the normal as it enters/ leaves glass.
◆ Make sure you can mark on a diagram of a wave the amplitude and the wavelength.
◆ Remember to convert other units of wave-length to metres before using the wave equation.

Equation to remember

wave speed	=	frequency	×	wavelength
(metre per second, m/s)		(hertz, Hz)		(metre, m)

Using waves

Key facts

Visible spectrum

◆ The visible spectrum is produced on passing white light through a prism because white light is made up of many different colours.

◆ Different colours of light are refracted by different amounts; red is refracted least and violet light most.

Sound and ultrasound

◆ Sounds are produced when objects vibrate.

◆ The greater the size (amplitude) of vibrations, the louder the sound.

◆ The higher the frequency of a sound, the higher its pitch.

◆ Ultrasonic waves have a frequency higher than the upper limit of the hearing range for humans.

Diagrams to remember

The visible spectrum

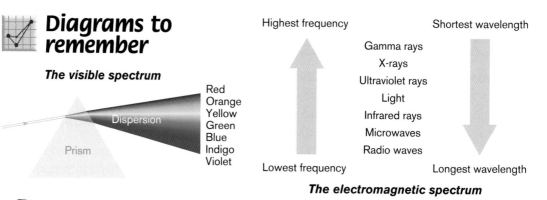

Red
Orange
Yellow
Green
Blue
Indigo
Violet

Dispersion

Prism

Highest frequency   Shortest wavelength

Gamma rays
X-rays
Ultraviolet rays
Light
Infrared rays
Microwaves
Radio waves

Lowest frequency   Longest wavelength

The electromagnetic spectrum

Important ideas

Effects of electromagnetic radiation on living tissues

◆ Microwaves are absorbed by the water in cells, which might be damaged or killed by the heat released.

◆ Infrared radiation is absorbed by skin and is felt as heat.

◆ Ultraviolet radiation can pass through skin to deeper tissues.

◆ X-radiation and gamma radiation mostly pass through soft tissues, but some can be absorbed by the cells.

◆ High doses of ultraviolet radiation, X-radiation and gamma radiation can kill normal cells.

◆ Lower doses of these types of ionising radiation can cause normal cells to become cancerous.

Uses of electromagnetic waves

Type of radiation	Uses
Radio waves	• to transmit radio and TV programmes between different points on the Earth's surface
Microwaves	• to send information to and from satellites • for cooking, since these wavelengths are strongly absorbed by water molecules
Infrared	• in grills, toasters and radiant heaters • in optical fibre communication • for the remote control of TV sets and VCRs
Visible light	• illumination
Ultraviolet	• in sun beds • in fluorescent lamps and security coding
X-rays	• to produce shadow pictures of materials that X-rays do not easily pass through, including bones and metals
Gamma rays	• to kill harmful bacteria in food • to sterilise surgical instruments • to kill cancer cells

Ultrasound

◆ Ultrasound is used for scanning internal structures in medicine and industry.
◆ The ultrasonic waves are partly reflected when they meet a boundary between two different media.
◆ The time taken for the reflections of ultrasonic pulses to reach a detector (usually placed near to the source) is a measure of how far away such a boundary is.
◆ Ultrasonic waves can clean delicate mechanisms without having to disassemble them — the pulses dislodge dust particles.

Using ultrasound to detect flaws in a metal block

Ultrasound generator
Ultrasound detector
Flaw

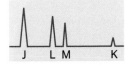

A pulse is sent from the generator through the block. The oscilloscope trace shows the time at which ultrasound reaches the detector.

J = ultrasound going straight from generator to detector
L = ultrasound reflected from left side of flaw
M = ultrasound reflected from right side of flaw
K = ultrasound reflected from right side of block

✖ Beware

◆ Don't confuse wavelength and frequency of these different electromagnetic waves — the longer the wavelength, the lower the frequency.

Seismic waves

🔑 Key facts

Structure of the Earth

◆ The Earth is nearly spherical and has a layered structure comprising:
  • a thin crust
  • a mantle extending almost halfway to the centre which has all the properties of a solid except that it can flow very slowly

• a core of just over half of the Earth's radius, made of nickel and iron, the outer part of which is liquid and the inner part of which is solid

◆ Earthquakes produce shock waves that might travel through these different layers.

◆ The shock waves move at different speeds through different layers.

📈 Diagrams to remember

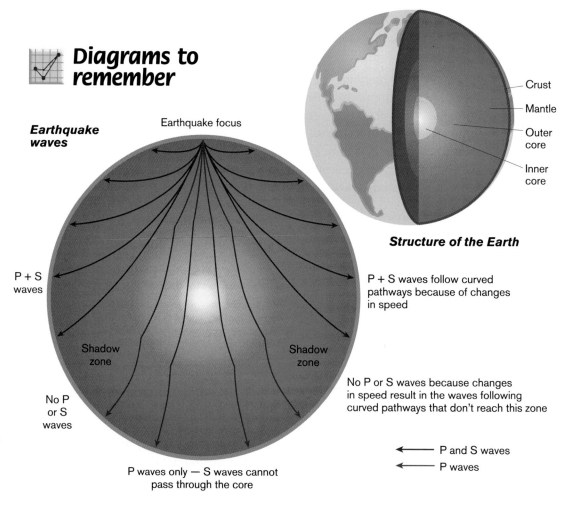

Earthquake waves

Earthquake focus

Structure of the Earth

Crust
Mantle
Outer core
Inner core

P + S waves

Shadow zone

Shadow zone

No P or S waves

P + S waves follow curved pathways because of changes in speed

No P or S waves because changes in speed result in the waves following curved pathways that don't reach this zone

P waves only — S waves cannot pass through the core

⟵ P and S waves
⟵ P waves

Important ideas

Seismic waves

- ◆ Shock waves from earth-quakes (seismic waves) travel through the Earth.
- ◆ These waves are detected using seismographs.
- ◆ Earthquakes produce surface waves that can cause earth-quake damage and two types of waves that can travel through the Earth:
  - • faster travelling **P waves**, which are **longitudinal** and travel through liquids as well as solids
  - • slower travelling **S waves** which are **transverse** and travel only through solids
- ◆ Both types of wave travel in curved paths as their speed changes gradually through a material.
- ◆ When the state of the trans-mitting medium changes abruptly, e.g. when moving from solid to liquid, the wave direction also changes abruptly.

Earthquake

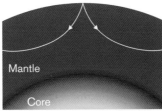

P waves speed up as they move through the mantle; this change in speed results in a curved pathway

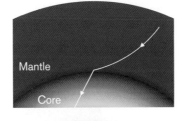

When P waves move from the semi-solid mantle to the liquid outer core they are refracted, bringing about a change of direction

S waves can only travel through solids, so they do not pass from the mantle into the outer core

During an earthquake, buildings vibrate vertically first; this is due to the arrival of the faster P waves, which are longitudinal waves

Shortly afterwards they vibrate horizontally due to the arrival of S waves, which are transverse waves

✖ Beware

- ◆ Revise your work on refraction before revising this section — the laws of refraction apply to P and S waves as well as to electromagnetic waves.

The solar system

🔑 Key facts

Planets and stars

- The Earth spins on its own axis once every day (24 hours).
- The half of the Earth that faces the sun is in daylight; the other half of the Earth is in darkness.
- The Earth moves round (orbits) the sun once each year (just over 365 days).

- The stars in the night sky stay in fixed patterns (called constellations).
- The planets that are visible to the naked eye look just like stars.
- Planets move very slowly across the constellations.
- We can see planets because they reflect light from the sun.

💡 Important ideas

Gravity and orbits

- The orbits of the planets are slightly squashed circles (ellipses) with the sun quite close to the centre.
- Comets have orbits that are far from circular. They are very much closer to the sun at some times than at others. This is when they can be seen.
- The further away an orbiting body is, the longer it takes to make a complete orbit.
- The Earth, the sun, the moon and all other bodies attract each other with a force called gravity.

Orbit of comet

Sun

Orbits of planets

Comet visible from Earth only when its orbit brings it close to the sun

- As the distance between two bodies increases, the force of gravity between them decreases more than in proportion to the increase in distance.
- A smaller body will stay in orbit around a larger one because of the balance between its high speed and the force of gravity between the bodies.
- To stay in orbit at a particular distance, smaller bodies must move at a particular speed around larger bodies.

Satellites

◆ Satellites can be put into orbit around the Earth. They can be used to:
  • send information between places that are a long way apart on Earth
  • monitor conditions on Earth, including the weather
  • observe the universe without the Earth's atmosphere getting in the way

A communication satellite is placed in orbit high above the equator

Its speed is adjusted so that it completes its orbit in 24 hours; this means that it stays in the same position relative to the Earth's surface — it is geostationary

◆ Communications satellites are usually put into an orbit high above the equator so that they move around the Earth at exactly the same rate as the Earth spins. This means that they are always in the same position when viewed from Earth (a **geostationary orbit**).

◆ **Monitoring satellites** are usually put into a low polar orbit so that the Earth spins beneath them and they can scan the whole Earth each day.

Monitoring satellites are placed in low polar orbits; the whole of the Earth's surface spins beneath them every day

Beware

◆ Make sure you understand *why* satellites stay in orbit.
◆ Make sure you understand *why* a geostationary satellite is always in the same position when viewed from Earth — what would you observe about a geostationary satellite if you viewed it from the moon?

The universe

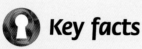

 Key facts

Galaxies

◆ Our sun is just one of millions of stars in a group of stars called the Milky Way galaxy.

◆ The stars in a galaxy are often millions of times further away from each other than the planets in the solar system.

◆ The universe as a whole is made up of at least a billion galaxies.

◆ Galaxies are often millions of times further apart than the stars within a galaxy.

◆ Stars are formed by gravitational forces.

◆ Most of the energy released in stars is the result of nuclear fusion reactions.

◆ This energy creates expansive forces.

◆ In a stable star, gravitational and expansive forces are balanced.

 **Important ideas**

The big-bang theory: evidence from elements

◆ During a star's lifetime, nuclei of lighter elements gradually fuse to produce nuclei of heavier elements.

◆ These nuclear fusion reactions release the energy that is radiated by stars.

◆ Nuclei of the heaviest elements are present in the sun, and atoms of these elements are present in the inner planets of the solar system.

◆ This suggests that the solar system was formed from the material produced when earlier stars exploded.

The big-bang theory: evidence from 'red-shift'

◆ Light from other galaxies is shifted to the red end of the spectrum.

◆ The further away galaxies are, the bigger this 'red-shift'.

◆ This can be explained by the fact that:
 • other galaxies are moving away from us very quickly
 • the further away from us a galaxy is, the faster it is moving away from us

◆ This suggests that the whole universe is expanding and that it might have started with a huge explosion ('big bang'), from one place, billions of years ago.

The life history of a star

- A star forms when enough dust and gas from space is pulled together by gravitational attraction.
- Stars are very massive, so the force of **gravity** that tends to draw together the matter from which they are made is very strong.
- The very high temperatures create forces that tend to make them expand.
- During the main stable period of a star, these forces are balanced.
- The star then expands to become a **red giant**.
- At a later point in its history the star contracts under its own gravity to become a **white dwarf**.
- The matter from which the star is made might then be millions of times denser than any matter on Earth.
- If a red giant is massive enough, it might eventually contract and then explode (to become a **supernova**), throwing dust and gas into space.
- The matter that is left behind might form a very dense **neutron star**.
- If enough matter is left behind, this might be so dense, and its gravitational field so strong, that nothing can escape from it — not even light or other forms of electromagnetic radiation. It is then called a **black hole**.

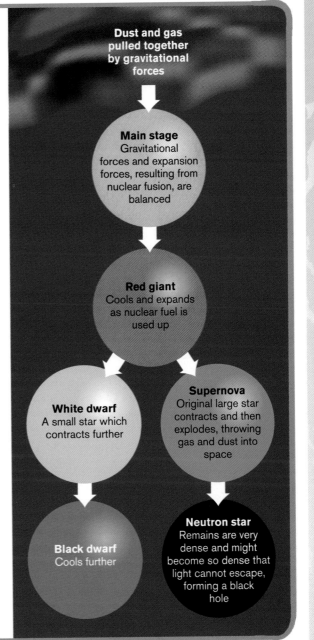

Dust and gas pulled together by gravitational forces

Main stage
Gravitational forces and expansion forces, resulting from nuclear fusion, are balanced

Red giant
Cools and expands as nuclear fuel is used up

White dwarf
A small star which contracts further

Supernova
Original large star contracts and then explodes, throwing gas and dust into space

Black dwarf
Cools further

Neutron star
Remains are very dense and might become so dense that light cannot escape, forming a black hole

✖ Beware

- Make sure you understand *the evidence* that leads many scientists to believe in the big-bang theory.
- Don't confuse nuclear fusion with nuclear fission — fusion is joining, fission is splitting.

Energy transfers and efficiency

🔑 Key facts

Energy transfers

◆ Whenever energy is transferred, only part of it is transferred to where it is wanted and in the form it is wanted (**usefully transferred**).

◆ The rest of the energy is transferred in some non-useful way and so is wasted.

◆ The energy that is 'wasted' during energy transfers and the energy that is usefully transferred both end up being transferred to the surroundings which become *warmer*.

Efficiency

◆ The more of the energy supplied to a device that is usefully transferred, the more **efficient** we say the device is.

📈 Diagrams to remember

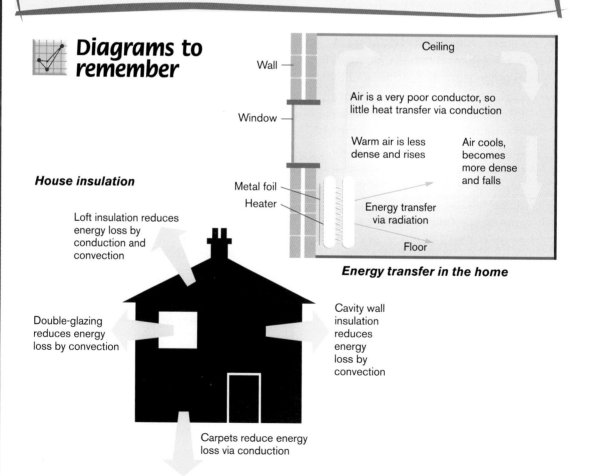

House insulation

Loft insulation reduces energy loss by conduction and convection

Double-glazing reduces energy loss by convection

Cavity wall insulation reduces energy loss by convection

Carpets reduce energy loss via conduction

Wall

Window

Metal foil

Heater

Ceiling

Air is a very poor conductor, so little heat transfer via conduction

Warm air is less dense and rises

Air cools, becomes more dense and falls

Energy transfer via radiation

Floor

Energy transfer in the home

Important ideas

Conduction

◆ Conduction is the transfer of energy by a substance, *without the substance itself moving*.
◆ Metals are very good conductors.
◆ Non-metals are usually poor conductors (insulators).
◆ Gases are very poor conductors.
◆ Conduction occurs in metals because the hotter the metal is, the more kinetic energy the **free electrons** in the metal structure have.
◆ This energy is transferred to cooler parts of a piece of metal by the free electrons as they diffuse through the metal and collide with ions and with other electrons.

Convection

◆ The transfer of energy by the *movement* of liquids or gases is called convection.
◆ Convection currents occur in liquids and gases because their particles move faster when they are hot, causing the liquid or gas to expand.
◆ Warm regions are then less dense than cold regions.
◆ The warm regions rise up through the colder regions and colder regions replace the warmer regions.

Radiation

◆ Thermal radiation is the transfer of energy by waves.
◆ Particles of matter are *not* involved.
◆ Hot bodies emit mainly infrared radiation.
◆ The hotter an object is, the more energy it radiates.
◆ Dark, matt surfaces emit more radiation than light, shiny surfaces at the same temperature.
◆ Dark, matt surfaces are good **absorbers** (poor reflectors) of radiation.
◆ Light, shiny surfaces are good **reflectors** (poor absorbers) of radiation.

✖ Beware

◆ *Don't* confuse the **absorption** and **emission** of radiation. A good absorber is usually a poor emitter and vice versa.
◆ There are *no units* for efficiency, so give your answer as a percentage or as a proportion of 1, for example 75% or 0.75.

Equation to remember

$$\text{efficiency} = \frac{\text{useful energy transferred by device}}{\text{total energy supplied to device}}$$

Energy resources

🔑 Key facts

Renewable and non-renewable energy resources

- The Earth's supply of the fossil fuels (coal, oil and gas) and of nuclear fuels is limited. Once they are used up they cannot be replaced. They are **non-renewable energy resources**.

- More trees can be grown to replace trees that are cut down to provide wood for fuel. Wood is a **renewable** energy resource.
- Renewable energy resources include
  - sunlight
  - wind
  - waves/running water
  - tides

💡 Important ideas

Generating electricity in power stations

- In most power stations, energy from fuel is used to heat water.
- Fuels include:
  - fossil fuels
  - nuclear fuel, mainly uranium and plutonium
- The steam produced is used to drive turbines.
- The turbines then drive generators which produce electricity.

Generating electricity from renewable energy resources

- Energy from renewable resources can be used to drive turbines directly using:
  - the wind
  - the rise and fall of water due to waves
  - the flow of water from a higher level to a lower level from behind tidal barrages or the dams of hydroelectric schemes
- In some volcanic areas, hot water and steam rise to the surface.
- The steam can be tapped and used to drive turbines, producing geothermal energy supplies.
- The energy released in volcanic areas originally came from the decay of radioactive elements, including uranium, within the Earth.
- Electricity can be produced directly from the sun's radiation using solar cells.

Disadvantages of using different energy resources

Energy resource	Disadvantages
Fossil fuels	Burning releases carbon dioxide, a gas that increases the greenhouse effect, causing increased global warming. Burning most types of coal and oil also releases sulphur dioxide, a gas that helps to produce acid rain.
Nuclear	If there is an accident, large amounts of very dangerous radioactive material might be released over a wide area. Nuclear power stations produce waste, some of which stays dangerously radioactive for thousands of years and has to be stored safely.
Wind	Groups of large wind generators (wind farms) are usually sited on hills and/or coasts and are considered unsightly by some people (visual pollution). They can also be noisy for people living nearby (noise pollution). They are unreliable in many areas.
Tides	Involves building barrages across river estuaries. This destroys the habitat of many organisms.
Hydroelectric	Damming upland river valleys means flooding land that may have previously been used for farming.
Solar	Compared with all other sources of electricity, solar cells have a very high cost per unit of electricity produced over their lifetime.

✓ Diagram to remember

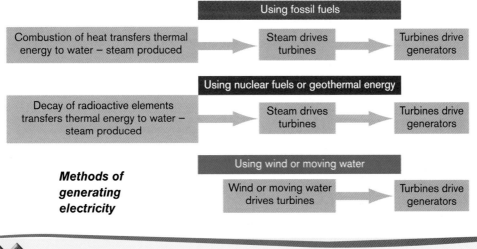

Methods of generating electricity

Using fossil fuels

Combustion of heat transfers thermal energy to water – steam produced → Steam drives turbines → Turbines drive generators

Using nuclear fuels or geothermal energy

Decay of radioactive elements transfers thermal energy to water – steam produced → Steam drives turbines → Turbines drive generators

Using wind or moving water

Wind or moving water drives turbines → Turbines drive generators

✖ Beware

◆ You will often be asked for advantages and disadvantages of using different energy sources to generate electricity. You will receive full marks only if you refer to more than one disadvantage and more than one advantage.

Work, power and energy

Key facts

- **Energy** is measured in **joules (J)**.
- On Earth the gravitational field strength is about 10 newtons per kilogram.

Diagram to remember

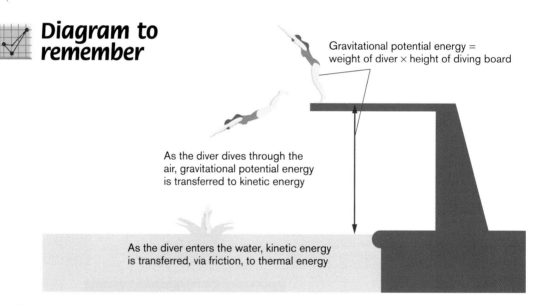

Gravitational potential energy = weight of diver × height of diving board

As the diver dives through the air, gravitational potential energy is transferred to kinetic energy

As the diver enters the water, kinetic energy is transferred, via friction, to thermal energy

Important ideas

Work

- When a force moves an object, energy is transferred and work is done:

  work done = energy transferred

Potential energy

- Gravitational potential energy is the energy *stored* in an object because of the height to which the object has been *lifted against the force of gravity*.
- Elastic potential energy is the energy stored in an elastic object when *work is done on the object to change its shape*.

Power
◆ Power is a measure of how *fast* energy is transferred.
◆ The greater the power, the more energy is transferred in a given time.

Kinetic energy
◆ Kinetic energy is the energy an object has because of its *movement*.
◆ An object has more kinetic energy:
  • the greater its mass
  • the greater its speed

Equations to remember

work done = force applied × distance moved in direction of force
(joule, J)   (newton, N)   (metre, m)

$$\text{power (watt, W)} = \frac{\text{work done (joule, J)}}{\text{time taken (second, s)}}$$

weight   =   mass   ×   gravitational field strength
(newton, N) (kilogram, kg)   (newton per kilogram, N/kg)

change in gravitational potential energy = weight × change in vertical height
(joule, J)   (newton, N)   (metre, m)

kinetic energy = $\frac{1}{2}$ × mass × (speed)^2
(joule, J)   (kilogram, kg) [(metre per second)^2, (m/s)^2]

✖ Beware
◆ *Don't* confuse mass with weight:
  • mass is the amount of matter in an object
  • weight is a force and is measured in newtons
◆ If the work done is lifting something, then the force applied equals the weight of the object.
◆ In the kinetic energy equation, *don't* confuse speed and acceleration. Acceleration (m/s^2) is *not* the same as (speed)^2 or (m/s)^2.

Radioactivity

Key facts

Types of radiation

- Alpha (α) radiation is easily absorbed by a few centimetres of air or a thin sheet of paper.
- Beta (β) radiation easily passes through air or paper but is mostly absorbed by a few millimetres of metal.
- Gamma (γ) radiation is very penetrating and requires many centimetres of lead or metres of concrete to absorb most of it.

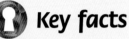 Important ideas

Half-life

- The rate of radioactive decay is measured by counting emissions from decaying radioactive elements.
- The half-life of a radioactive substance is the time it takes for the number of parent atoms in a sample to halve.
- It is also the time it takes for the count rate from the original substance to fall to half its initial level.
- To calculate half-life, find the time taken for the count rate to halve by interpolating from a half-life graph. For example, in this case from 80 counts to 40 counts takes 10 minutes.
- You may also be given the half-life and asked to calculate the fraction remaining after a stated time. In this case the half-life is 10 minutes; after 3 half-lives (30 minutes) one eighth remains (80→10).

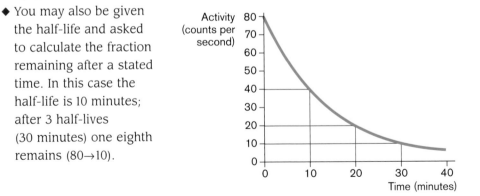

Using radiation to monitor thickness
◆ As radiation passes through a material it can be absorbed.
◆ The greater the thickness of a material, the greater the absorption.

Using radiation to monitor the uniformity of metal foil during its manufacture

Background radiation
◆ There are radio-active substances all around us:
  • in the ground
  • in the air
  • in building materials
  • in food
  • from space

Effects of radiation on living tissue
◆ When radiation from radioactive materials collides with neutral atoms or molecules these can become charged (ionised).
◆ When radiation ionises molecules in living cells it can cause damage, sometimes leading to cancer.
◆ Higher doses of ionising radiation can kill cells, including cancer cells and harmful microorganisms.
◆ When sources of radiation are *outside* the body:
  • beta and gamma radiation are the most dangerous because they can reach the cells
  • alpha radiation is least dangerous because it is unlikely to reach living cells
◆ When sources of radiation are *inside* the body:
  • alpha radiation is the most dangerous because it is so strongly absorbed by cells
  • beta and gamma radiations are less dangerous because cells are less likely to absorb the radiation

✖ Beware
◆ Practise doing half-life calculations both from figures and from graphs. Always remember to subtract background rate from count rate to obtain the true rate.
◆ Be careful to distinguish between the effects of radiation when the source is inside the body and when it is outside the body.

Nuclear fission

🔑 Key facts

Structure of the atom

Particle	Relative mass	Relative charge
Proton	1	+1
Neutron	1	0
Electron	Negligible	−1

Atomic number and mass number

◆ All atoms of a particular element have the same number of protons.
◆ Atoms of different elements have different numbers of protons.
◆ The number of protons in an atom is called its **atomic number** (proton number).

◆ The total number of protons and neutrons in an atom is called its **mass number**.
◆ Atoms of the same element can have different numbers of neutrons; these atoms are called **isotopes** of that element.

Types of radiation

◆ Alpha radiation consists of helium nuclei — particles made up of two protons and two neutrons.
◆ Beta radiation consists of electrons emitted from the nuclei of atoms. For each electron emitted, a neutron in the nucleus becomes a proton.
◆ Gamma radiation is very short-wavelength electromagnetic radiation.

💡 Important ideas

Radiation

◆ Radioactive isotopes are atoms with unstable nuclei.
◆ When an unstable nucleus splits up (disintegrates):
  • it emits radiation
  • a different atom, with a different number of protons, is formed
◆ For example, uranium in rocks decays to form lead, and radioactive iodine (used as a tracer) decays to form xenon.

Fission

◆ Nuclear fission is used in nuclear reactors.
◆ When an atom with a very large nucleus is bombarded with neutrons:
  • the nucleus splits into two smaller nuclei
  • further neutrons are released which might cause further nuclear fission, resulting in a chain reaction
  • the new atoms which are formed are themselves radioactive

Uses of fission

◆ The energy released by an atom during radioactive disintegration or nuclear fission is very large compared with the energy released when a chemical bond is made between two atoms. This is why only very small amounts of nuclear fuel are needed in nuclear power stations.

◆ During one half-life, half of the radioactive atoms initially present in a sample decay. This idea can be used to date materials.

◆ Uranium isotopes decay to produce stable isotopes of lead. The relative proportions of uranium and lead isotopes in a sample of igneous rock can, therefore, be used to date the rock.

◆ The proportions of the radioisotope potassium-40 and its stable decay product argon can also be used to date igneous rocks from which the gaseous argon has been unable to escape.

Diagrams to remember

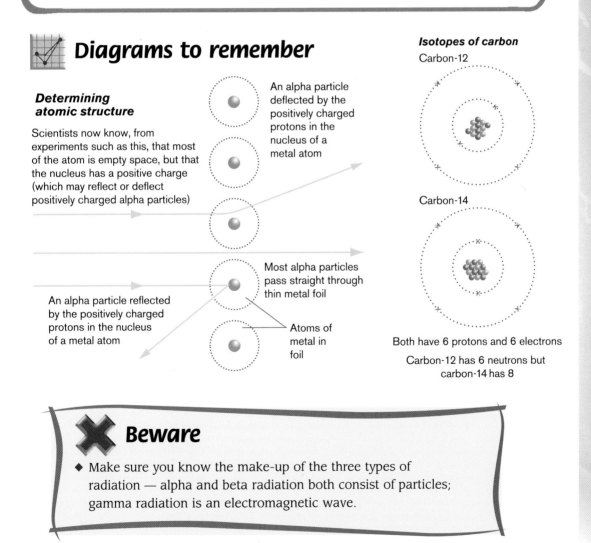

Isotopes of carbon

Carbon-12

Determining atomic structure

Scientists now know, from experiments such as this, that most of the atom is empty space, but that the nucleus has a positive charge (which may reflect or deflect positively charged alpha particles)

An alpha particle deflected by the positively charged protons in the nucleus of a metal atom

Most alpha particles pass straight through thin metal foil

An alpha particle reflected by the positively charged protons in the nucleus of a metal atom

Atoms of metal in foil

Carbon-14

Both have 6 protons and 6 electrons

Carbon-12 has 6 neutrons but carbon-14 has 8

Beware

◆ Make sure you know the make-up of the three types of radiation — alpha and beta radiation both consist of particles; gamma radiation is an electromagnetic wave.